THE SCIENCE OF BIOLOGY SERIES
No 1

Edited by J. D. Carthy, M.A., Ph.D., F.I.Biol.,
Scientific Director of the Field Studies Council

and J. F. Sutcliffe, B.Sc., Ph.D., D.Sc.,
Professor of Plant Physiology, University of Sussex

The Biology of Mosquito-Borne Disease

P. F. MATTINGLY

Principal Scientific Officer
British Museum, (Natural History)

The Biology
of
Mosquito-Borne
Disease

'Mosquitoes do not surrender to Elephants' *Walter Lippmann*

London
GEORGE ALLEN AND UNWIN LTD
New York
AMERICAN ELSEVIER PUBLISHING COMPANY, INC

Standard Book Number 444-19723-0

Library of Congress Catalog Card Number 70-93924

American Edition published by
American Elsevier Publishing Company, Inc.
52 Vanderbilt Avenue, New York, New York 10017

Acknowledgements

WITH the exception of Fig. 42, all line-drawings are the author's. Where they have been redrawn from published material the source is indicated in the accompanying legend. Thanks are due to the following for supplying original photographs and for permission to reproduce them.

Figure 42: Dr Mario Coluzzi and the editors of *Parassitologia*
Plate   IA   Mr. J. S. Haeger
Plate   IB   Dr T. Orihel and the Tulane University Primate Research Center
Plate   II   Dr F. R. S. Kellett and Insect Vector Control Division, Medical Department, Trinidad
Plate   IVA   Dr W. W. Macdonald
          B   Dr Pedro Galindo and the Williams & Wilkins Company, Baltimore, Md
Plate   VA   Professor H. E. Hinton
          B   Dr M. W. Provost and Mr J. S. Haeger and the Entomological Society of America; photography by Joe O'Neal and J. S. Haeger
Plate   VI   Drs M. W. Provost and J. S. Haeger and, for B, the American Mosquito Control Association; photography by J. S. Haeger
Plate VIIA   Dr A. J. Haddow and the Information Department, East African Community
Plate VIII   Professor J. D. Gillett and the East African Virus Research Institute, Entebbe
Plate IXA   Dr R. H. Wharton and the editors, *Medical Journal of Malaya*
          B   Dr J. de Zulueta and the Williams & Wilkins Company, Baltimore, Md

Plate X   Dr M. T. Gillies and the editor, *Bulletin of Entomological Research*
Plate XIA   Dr Mario Coluzzi
       B   Dr Mario Coluzzi and the Elsevier Publishing Company, Amsterdam, Netherlands
Plate XIIA   Dr M. T. Gillies

Figures 45 and 46 are from an original document and a water-colour in the British Museum (Natural History). Permission to reproduce the former and redraw the latter was granted by the Keeper of Entomology acting on behalf of the Trustees.

Dr George Davidson provided up-to-date records for inclusion in Figure 43. Miss Beryl Wheeler (Mrs S. R. Mattingly) gave valuable professional help with arranging and re-photographing material for the plates. It is impossible to thank individually all those others who, over the years and in many countries, have contributed directly or indirectly to the production of this book. Their help and companionship are, however, deeply felt and are no mean example of international brotherhood in the pursuit of a common aim.

Contents

Plates

Introduction

THE history of medical entomology, as a science, dates from 1877. In that year Manson demonstrated, for the first time, the development of a human parasite, *Wuchereria bancrofti*, in a mosquito, *Culex pipiens fatigans*. The most distinguished of living medical entomologists, Sir Rickard Christophers, was four years old at the time, so that the entire history of our subject may be said, with truth, to span a single lifetime. During that period development has proceeded at an accelerating pace, so that at the present time more than a thousand papers are published annually on the subject of mosquitoes and mosquito-borne disease. As an example of the rapid growth of only one branch of the subject, it was possible, in 1953, to review the whole of mosquito genetics, quite adequately, in seventy-five pages. In 1967 it required a monograph with nearly 800.

The task of reviewing so extensive a literature has been formidable and the result must necessarily reflect some personal bias, in this case in the direction of entomology. Nevertheless an attempt has been made to give adequate representation, also, to parasitology and human biology, in the belief that it is only in the light of these that the implications of vector biology can be fully understood. The politics and economics of the matter have been largely ignored but a few facts and figures may help to set the stage.

The greatest single achievement in our ninety years of history has been the progress, however incomplete, of world-wide malaria eradication, rendering huge areas free from the threat of the disease. At the same time political, economic and administrative, as well as technical, considerations render many areas, notably almost all tropical Africa, open only to pre-eradication research, education and development. While this is so every success brings with it an open-ended commitment to maintenance and surveillance. Insecticide resistance, resulting, it seems, in many cases, from agricultural rather than medical insecticiding, continues to pose new and formidable problems. In the final battle a variety of weapons may have to be used, backed by a co-ordinated strategy. In this computers may have a vital part to play, but the decisive factor will be the brains behind them.

Malaria, once thought to be responsible for 300 million cases annually, may now have fallen behind filariasis as a progenitor of human ills. This disease is currently estimated to be responsible for upwards of 200 million cases at a given time, with the number increasing daily. So far as urban filariasis, in particular, is concerned we appear to be advancing rapidly backwards. Deteriorating standards of sanitation, coupled with uncontrolled urbanization and industrialization, have led to frightening pullulations of the urban vector, *C. p. fatigans*. This mosquito is currently estimated to occur in Rangoon in a density of 15 million per km.[2]

Filariasis is an insidious disease appearing only slowly in the form of gross disfigurement or disablement. In the sphere of the virus diseases recent developments have been nothing if not dramatic. Nineteen hundred and fifty-nine witnessed the initial outbreak of the first human mosquito-borne virus disease, Onyongnyong fever, ever to be associated with anopheline mosquitoes as major (indeed the only) vectors. The disease spread southwards, from north-west Uganda as far as Malawi, involving, on its way, more than a million cases. Though the most pathogenic of its particular group of viruses it was not, fortunately, lethal, merely painful, debilitating, frightening and temporarily crippling. Between 1960 and 1962, confining ourselves for the moment to Africa, there occurred in southern Ethiopia incomparably the greatest yellow fever epidemic ever recorded in that continent, with more than 200,000 cases and more than 30,000 deaths. A sinister element in the situation is that this outbreak occurred, so far as we know, some hundreds of miles nearer than ever before to Asia, from which continent yellow fever has so far been absent for reasons upon which one can only speculate.

Asia has not, however, been spared in other respects. In 1954 there occurred in Manila, and perhaps also in Bangkok, an apparently new, haemorrhagic form of dengue, lethal, unlike classical dengue, especially to children. Larger outbreaks followed and the disease has since spread westwards as far as India, showing signs of becoming permanently established in southern Asia. It is caused, so far as can be ascertained, by one or more of the classical dengue viruses and transmitted by the classical vector, *Aedes aegypti*. The causes of its sudden assumption of malignancy are unknown. Chikungunya virus, discovered in Tanzania in 1952, was detected, for the first time in Asia, in Bangkok in 1958. It occurred in epidemic form in Calcutta in 1963 and in the following year was responsible for nearly 400,000 cases (more than 20 per cent of the population) in Madras. An epidemic in Nagpur in 1965 is thought to have involved more than 40 per cent of the population of some sections of the city. Less dramatic but cumulatively far from negligible are the annual toll extorted by jungle yellow fever in South America and the repeated, sporadic outbreaks of encephalitis in North American cities and of a score of other mosquitoborne virus diseases in different parts of the world.

One misapprehension at least will, it is hoped, be avoided in the following pages, namely that our present knowledge and means of control are adequate and all that is needed is the will to go out and do battle. The realities are vastly more complex than that. Success can only come, if it comes at all, from a determination to maintain the progress already made in the face of a welter of conflicting interests and ultimately to arrive, through a deeper understanding of the problems confronting us, at a just assignment of priorities.

I

Diseases as Ecological Systems

DISEASES are not just collections of signs and symptoms calling for treatment by a physician. There are other, equally valid, ways of looking at them. From the viewpoint of public health and preventive medicine even such unlikely conditions as mental disorder, malignant disease and genetic disability may be seen as ecological systems involving human populations and their physical and biological environment. This is a more cheerful point of view than the purely clinical one, because it inspires the hope not merely of curing diseases when they occur but of preventing their occurrence and even, it may be, ultimately abolishing them altogether. Finding ways of doing this, and putting them into practice, involves many biological disciplines of which medicine, in the strict sense, is only one.

Even seemingly simple disease systems prove to be quite complicated when we look into them deeply enough. Thus a disease-causing organism or pathogen may be transferred from one person to another simply by a sneeze. Yet a variety of factors, social, behavioural, climatic, immunological, may combine to determine whether this happens often enough for the pathogen to become established or to build up and cause an epidemic. Arthropod-borne diseases are especially complicated because they involve an additional component, the arthropod vector by which the disease is carried from one human host to another. Such a vector is itself subject to environmental hazards which determine whether it will live long enough for the pathogen which it is carrying to mature and become infective. Still more complications arise in those diseases, called zoonoses, in which the pathogen is harboured by other animals as well as by man (Fig. 1).

Such complexity may seem rather daunting and it is true that, in the past, errors have occurred through oversimplification. On the other hand, the more complicated the system the greater the number of

B

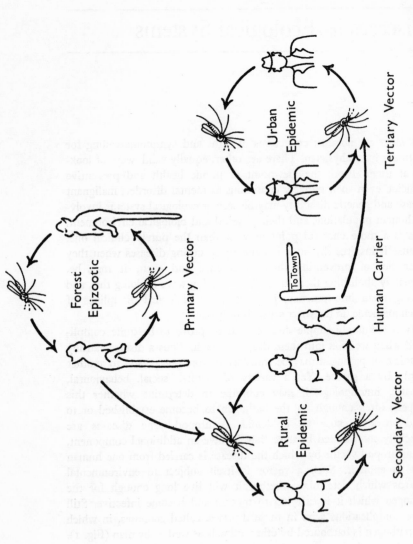

Fig. 1 A simple mosquito-borne zoonosis. Many varieties are known. Birds or any of several orders of mammals may act as primary hosts. Domestic animals may intervene as secondary hosts. The essential feature, in all cases, is the conveying by a mosquito, of the pathogen from another species of animal to man.

targets for attack. This is one reason for seeking the fullest possible understanding of the systems we are trying to disrupt. Another is the desirability of combining our various weapons to the best possible effect. This does not mean, of course, that we are justified in introducing complexity where none exists. Mosquito literature is, on the whole, mercifully free from the futile word-spinning which disfigures the literature relating to some other forms of anthropod-borne disease. Some definitions will be needed if we are to make clear the roles of the various major components. We shall try, however, to keep these as few and simple as possible, believing strongly that any other procedure can lead only to confusion and misconception.

The Nature of Host-pathogen Relations

That the relation of mosquito-borne pathogens to their human host is one of parasitism is unquestioned. They are smaller than man. They are metabolically dependent on him and they cause him damage for which they make no recompense. Their relationship to the arthropod vector is less obvious and has been the subject of some dispute. To elucidate it we shall need to examine the nature of parasitism more closely. The problems of defining this condition are notorious.[1] There is general agreement that it involves the exploitation of one organism, the host, by another, the parasite. Yet even this apparently simple concept involves conflicting elements. On the one hand there is dependence of the parasite on the host and, on the other, damage inflicted on the host by the parasite. The two do not necessarily go together. It is quite possible to envisage a host which has become totally immune to the effects of the parasite and on which, at the same time, the parasite is wholly dependent. This is, indeed, the climax to which evolving host-parasite systems are supposed to tend.

Parasitologists are concerned chiefly with the metabolic dependence of the parasite on the host and the morphological and physiological consequences for the parasite that this entails.[2] In the particular systems with which we are concerned this factor of metabolic dependence is always present. There exist certain other systems in which the situation is ambiguous. An example is mosquito-borne myxomatosis of rabbits in which the prolonged survival of the pathogen on the mouthparts of the vector suggests something more than a purely mechanical relationship though, in fact, nothing more has proved demonstrable. There are also cases of simple phoresy, such as the occasional transport by mosquitoes of human body lice or the remarkable form of myiasis caused by burrowing larvae of the fly *Dermatobia hominis*. In this case the female fly seizes a mosquito of the genus *Psorophora* and firmly glues her eggs to its abdomen. After recovering from the shock the mosquito flies off and when it visits a subsequent host the eggs hatch rapidly and the *Dermatobia* larvae burrow into the skin.

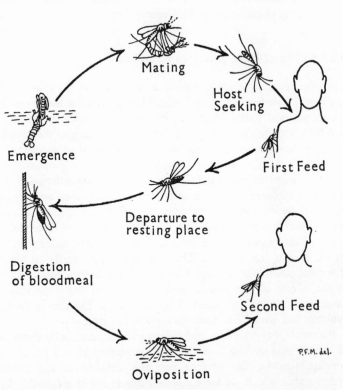

Fig. 2 Initiation of the transmission cycle. In the case of the mosquito-borne viruses a single reproductive cycle of the mosquito may suffice, under optimal conditions, for maturation of the pathogen. In general, however, several cycles elapse before the first infective blood-meal. During this time the vector is subject to many hazards, so that damage inflicted by the pathogen would be a disadvantage to both.

Apart from these somewhat outré examples, all the different kinds of pathogen with which we shall be dealing are dependent on the mosquito not only for dissemination but for maturation. Direct transfer of a mosquito-borne virus, on the freshly infected mouthparts, may sometimes occur. A few pathogens of this type have been known to cause accidental infection by inhalation or entry into abrasions. Infection with malaria during blood transfusion is a factor seriously to be reckoned with. But these are sporadic events and quite insufficient for the maintenance of any of the human mosquito-borne pathogens in nature. In all of these, with the solitary exception of myiasis, mentioned above, the infective stages are reached only after an obligatory period of development within the vector. Even the mosquito-borne viruses exhibit a period of latency after uptake by the vector and until this is over transmission is impossible.

Having regard to this dependence on the vector for shelter, it is easy to see why the element of damage to the vector by the pathogen should be largely absent. While the mosquito is bringing the pathogen to maturity it has to pass through at least one reproductive cycle, usually several, with all the risks attendant of blood-feeding, oviposition and location of the host and oviposition site (Fig. 2). If it is to survive these hazards and remain sufficiently active to deliver the pathogen to a new host, it must sustain as little damage from the pathogen as possible. Nevertheless, harmless though it may be to the vector, the whole gain from the relationship remains on the side of the pathogen, which thus qualifies as a parasite of the mosquito on the score both of metabolic dependence and of exploitation.

Further discussion has centred on the question whether the mosquito should be regarded as a parasite or a predator. Predators are usually thought of as active, free-living animals satisfying their needs by occasional raids on their prey alternating with relatively prolonged periods of quiescence. The description fits blood-feeding mosquitoes admirably and embodies aspects of their life and behaviour which are central to the problem of their control. Against this it has been argued that, in natural communities, predators form the apex of a 'pyramid of numbers', the members of which, at all levels except the lowest, feed on smaller and more numerous animals than themselves. In parasite systems, on the other hand, the pyramid is inverted with the smallest members, the parasites, feeding on larger and less numerous animals than themselves.

There is thus some reason for arguing that, ecologically, mosquitoes are parasites rather than predators. Neither interpretation seems adequate to express their whole nature. It seems preferable to accept that blood-feeding arthropods, in general, have some characteristics of predators and some of parasites. As a group they present a wide spectrum of adaptation to predation on the one hand and parasitism on the other. Within this spectrum mosquitoes conform more nearly to predators than do any other arthropods feeding on vertebrates. This despite the fact that it is customary to refer to the animals on which they feed as their 'hosts'. We shall see this position within the spectrum is largely responsible for the special nature of mosquito-borne disease.

The Vector concept

Although there is some disagreement as to the limits within which the term 'vector' can be properly applied, there is no disagreement as to its general significance. It simple means the carrier of a pathogen from one host to another. The only serious argument which has been advanced against its use with respect to mosquitoes is that it does not express the whole relation between mosquito and pathogen. As we have seen, the mosquito is not simply a 'flying hypodermic'. It also provides a nursery for certain stages of the parasite without which its life-history could not be completed. All that need be said in reply to this is that the term 'vector' is not intended to embrace all aspects of the mosquito-pathogen relation. Nor is there any reason why it should. When we describe a mosquito as a vector we do not thereby obscure or deny the fact that it is also a host. In any particular context we are perfectly justified in singling out that aspect of the mosquito which is relevant to our theme.

Before describing some of the special features of mosquitoes as vectors we must mention a further aspect of the vector concept which has sometimes been overlooked with unfortunate results. All vector populations are genetically heterogeneous. It follows that individuals composing them differ both in their intrinsic ability to harbour pathogens and in their response to extrinsic factors affecting transmission. In describing any species as a vector we are adopting a legitimate, but dangerous, form of shorthand. What we really mean is that some, but not necessarily all, individuals of that species are capable of transmitting the pathogen. We cannot say more.

Two major classes of vectors can be distinguished. They are the free-flying vectors (most Diptera and, perhaps, reduviid bugs) and the wingless vectors (mites, ticks, fleas, cimicid bugs, lice, wingless Diptera). The distinction bears an obvious relation to that already drawn between predatory and parasitic blood-feeding arthropods. It embodies fundamental features of the vector-pathogen relationship such as the diminished environmental hazards (offset by diminished powers of dissemination) attendant on winglessness. The distribution of different kinds of pathogens as between the two sorts of vectors suggests that it has been a major factor in the evolution of vector-parasite systems.

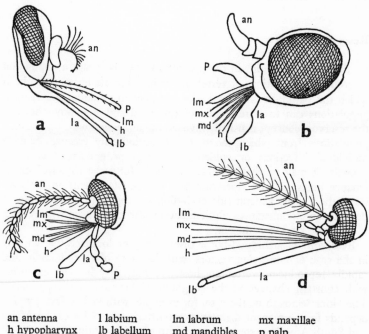

| an antenna | l labium | lm labrum | mx maxillae |
| h hypopharynx | lb labellum | md mandibles | p palp |

Fig. 3 Mouthparts of blood-feeding Diptera: **a** Tsetse fly, **b** Tabanid, **c** Ceratopogonid, **d** Mosquito. Blood-feeding muscids, such as tsetse flies have their mouthparts quite differently constructed from those of the others which are basically very similar.

In the mosquitoes, predation reaches a degree of refinement unknown in other blood-feeding Diptera. In the latter the mouthparts are relatively short and stout. Feeding is by the creation of a small pit or sump from which the blood and lymph are imbibed. This is called pool-feeding. In mosquitoes the mouthparts are longer and more slender (Fig. 3).[3] They are inserted direct into a capillary, markedly reducing the time needed for engorgement. The long legs and slender build are correlated characters.

In conclusion it may be noted that the term 'vector' need not apply exclusively to the invertebrate host. We admit this, by inference, when we find it necessary to qualify it with the term 'arthropod'. An infected person, travelling from place to place, is also a vector. It is more usual to describe him as a 'carrier' but there is no very good reason for this. The two words mean the same.

Reservoir Hosts

By the term 'reservoir', in the present context, is meant a population or group of populations of vertebrate or invertebrate hosts, or both, in which the pathogen is endemic, i.e. permanently maintained. Human populations can form reservoirs of this kind and sometimes do, but the reservoir concept is usually invoked in connection with non-human populations from which the pathogen periodically escapes, causing individual infections or epidemics in man or epizootics in other animals. It may be that vertebrates usually form the principal maintenance hosts in such reservoirs but, despite statements to the contrary, there is no general rule excluding arthropods from this role. It depends on circumstances. Both situations can occur even with respect to the same kind of pathogen.

Reservoirs of arthropod-borne disease may be localized, particularly in the case of non-flying vectors, with low rate of reproduction, and rapidly reproducing vertebrate hosts, or they may be very extensive with constant changes in the geographical location of the pathogen. The latter seems to be the case, for example, with yellow fever, which depends for permanent maintenance on huge forested areas in Africa and South America extensive enough to afford a continuous supply of fresh, susceptible vertebrate hosts. It is thought that at one time the same requirement may have been met by the larger, densely crowded cities of the Caribbean area in which the virus was endemic in the human population (p. 170).

a

P.F.M. del.

b

P.F.M. del.

Fig. 4. Habitat and disease. **a** Grass swamp and open paddy in north-western Malaya associated with periodic brugian filariasis. **b** Swamp forest in eastern Malaya associated with the subperiodic form of the disease. **a** based on Reid et al., *Ann. trop. Med. Parasit.*, 56: 323, 1962, **b** based on Wharton, ref. 5, p. 82.

As we already saw, adequate life-expectancy on the part of the vector is crucial for the maintenance of the pathogen. We shall deal with methods of assessing such life-expectancy later (p. 137). Life expectancy of the vertebrate host is equally important in principle but, in practice, tends to become important mainly under epidemic or epizootic conditions. More important in the maintenance of an enzootic reservoir are susceptibility of the vertebrate host and correlated factors affecting reproductive turnover and the supply of non-immunes.

These are factors governing the survival of the pathogen in its hosts. In a rather different category are those factors, mainly behavioural, which affect its transmission from one host to another. Some of these, such as dispersal of vectors, social aggregation of vertebrate hosts and mutual choice of habitat, affect the coincidence of host and vector in space. Others affect their coincidence in time. Chief among these are the cyclical behaviour patterns common to all vertebrate and invertebrate animals.

Finally account must be taken of the physical and biological environment in which these factors operate. For the vector microclimatic factors are critical. These are largely dependent on vegetation and this, in turn, on larger factors of climate and terrain. Climate operates directly in determining the seasonal availability of breeding places and requirements for hibernation or aestivation. A measure of the reality of the ecological aspect of disease is its constant, predictable association with habitat (Fig. 4). This is strikingly apparent even in the case of arthropod-borne viruses with their total dependence on residence in living cells.

The Role of Immunity

So much present day research is devoted to the mechanisms by which immunity is produced that immunology is sometimes treated as no more than a branch of biochemistry. This is a very narrow view. In many contexts it has equal claims to be regarded as a branch of ecology.[4] Active immunity, acquired by direct experience of the pathogen (as opposed to passive immunity acquired, e.g., by inheritance from the parents), is a valuable indicator of the past history of an infection in a given population. The development of the laboratory mouse as a test animal for the detection of neutralizing antibodies, during the 1930s, was the foundation for much of our present knowledge of the distribution of mosquito-borne viruses, their host range and, in certain cases, their association with particular occupations or environments. Recently more economical techniques have come to the fore, employing tissue cultures rather than whole animals. Still more recently success has at last been achieved in the growth of viruses in cultures of embryonic mosquito tissue. Such techniques may in future throw light on the still little understood problem of susceptibility to infection as between different species of vector. In the case of the other major groups of mosquito-borne pathogens, the malaria parasites and the filarioid nematodes, important advances have been made in the use of antigens prepared from parasites of laboratory animals for the rapid and economical survey of human populations. On the microcosmic scale, the development of immunological techniques of great refinement has rendered possible an insight into the changes in antigenicity exhibited by successive generations of malaria parasite in their battle with the immune mechanisms of the host.

Yet, valuable as these techniques unquestionably are, their application and the interpretation of the results which they yield demands and will continue to demand ecological insight of a high order. If this is true of the study of human populations it is even truer of studies of non-human hosts. Some idea of the problems involved can be gained from accounts of the early work on wild hosts of yellow fever.[5]

The Evolutionary Background

One of the most remarkable features of arthropod-borne disease systems is their resilience in the face of the increasingly powerful weapons directed against them by man. This resilience derives from the fact that the components of such systems have evolved together during long periods of time while the evolution of each has both conditioned and been conditioned by the others. The development of the ecological approach to disease has been accompanied by growing interest in the evolutionary background (reinforced, on very practical grounds, by the constant discovery of new zoonoses). In the chapters immediately following we shall consider some implications of the evolution of individual components for our understanding of disease systems as we encounter them today.

REFERENCES

1. DOGIEL, V. A., 1964, *General Parasitology*. 3rd Edn. London: Oliver & Boyd.
2. SMYTH, J. D., 1962, *Introduction to Animal Parasitology*. London: English Universities Press.
3. SNODGRASS, R. E., 1943, The feeding apparatus of biting and disease-carrying flies; a wartime contribution to medical entomology. *Smithson. misc. Collns*, 104 (1).
4. BURNET, F. M., 1962, *Natural History of Infectious Diseases*. Cambridge University Press.
5. STRODE, G. K., (Ed.), 1951, *Yellow Fever*. New York: McGraw Hill.

II

Evolution and Classification of Mosquito-borne Pathogens

MOSQUITO-BORNE pathogens, like other parasites, present special difficulties to the taxonomist. This is due, in part, to the absence of any fossil record and, in part, to a lack of distinctive morphological characters, probably implying extensive evolutionary convergence. These difficulties have been met in different ways in classifying the various groups. In the viruses reliance is placed exclusively on serological affinities as revealed by the presence or absence of common antigens. The result is a simple and eminently practical classification well suited to the needs of a branch of science which, except in special instances, is still in the descriptive stage. In contrast to this the classification of the malaria parasites and their allies leans heavily, even at the generic level, on details of life-history and associations with particular tissues of the vertebrate host. The filarioid nematodes offer better morphological criteria but even here there has been extensive convergence and, in the construction of higher categories, a great deal of reliance is placed on biological characters. For our purposes it is unnecessary to go very deeply into taxonomic questions, particularly those relating to morphology. We shall simply give a brief outline of current ideas regarding evolutionary relationships as an introduction to parasite taxonomy and the general nature of host and vector relations.

Taxonomy and Phylogeny of Malaria Parasites

The idea that the malaria parasites originated as parasites or commensals of arthropods is no longer widely held. It is now generally believed that they originated from primitive eimeriine, or, more probably, adeleine, coccidians parasitizing the vertebrate gut.[1] This does not, of course, rule out a still earlier origin of the coccidians from parasites of invertebrates. Such an origin seems more than probable. There are very few parasites of Protozoa or coelenterates, none at all, so far as is known, of sponges, but parasitism seems to have become widespread with the attainment of the annelid level of organization. The many present-day two-host systems involving marine gregarines, annelids and molluscs may well resemble in general features the sorts of systems from which the ancestors of the malaria parasites were derived by swallowing of the invertebrate host.

Those eimeriine and adeleine coccidians from which the malaria parasites are thought to have evolved resemble them in having both a vertebrate and a blood-feeding invertebrate host. The latter becomes infected while taking the blood-meal but infection of the vertebrate is by the swallowing of the invertebrate. In the malaria parasites (Plasmodiidae) and their supposedly more primitive relatives, the Haemoproteidae, the infective stages (sporozoites) are injected directly into the vertebrate bloodstream. The Haemoproteidae differ from the Plasmodiidae in undergoing multiplication (schizogony) only in endothelial cells or liver parenchyma. In the Plasmodiidae additional schizogonic cycles take place in the vertebrate red blood-cells. It is therefore argued that there have been two major steps in evolution producing three evolutionary grades, the haemogregarine (or eimeriine), haemoproteid, and plasmodiid (Fig. 5).

One school of thought derives the malaria parasites from eimeriine coccidians (Lankesterellidae) parasitizing amphibians and reptiles. Although the invertebrate hosts are blood-feeders (leeches, mites), infection of the vertebrate is by the oral route. The entire development of the parasite takes place in the vertebrate intestinal wall or the endothelial cells of the blood-vessels, according to genus. Sporogony takes place in the vertebrate and the sporozoites enter the blood-cells and are taken up by the invertebrate during feeding. They then pass, without visible change, into the next vertebrate host which swallows the invertebrate. This is quite different from the situation in the plasmodiids and haemoproteids, where infection of the invertebrate is by gametocytes while gamete formation, fertilization and sporogony all take place in the vector.

For this reason it is preferred to derive the malaria parasites from adeleine haemogregarines, while treating the Lankesterellidae as an evolutionary sideline. In the adeleines infection of the vector is by gametocytes and infection of the vertebrate, by the oral route, leads to establishment either in endothelial cells, as in *Karyolysus* of lizards, or in liver parenchyma, as in *Hepatozoon* of reptiles, birds and mammals. Malaria parasites of birds and reptiles undergo schizogony

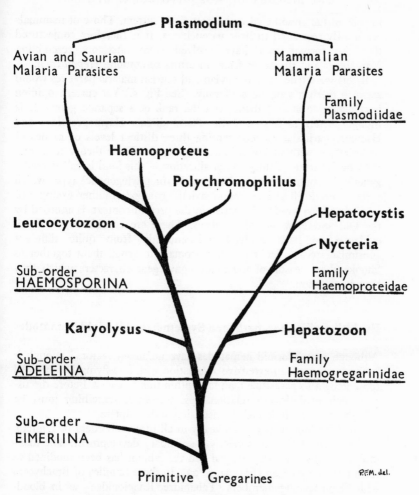

Plasmodium

Avian and Saurian
Malaria Parasites

Mammalian
Malaria Parasites

Family
Plasmodiidae

Haemoproteus

Polychromophilus

Hepatocystis

Leucocytozoon

Nycteria

Sub-order
HAEMOSPORINA

Family
Haemoproteidae

Karyolysus

Hepatozoon

Sub-order
ADELEINA

Family
Haemogregarinidae

Sub-order
EIMERIINA

Primitive Gregarines

P.F.M. del.

Fig. 5 Evolution of malaria parasites. Three evolutionary grades are postulated. In the haemogregarines infection is by ingestion. In haemoproteids infection is by injection into the bloodstream, but multiplication of the parasite takes place only in fixed tissue cells. Finally, in plasmodiids multiplication takes place also in blood-cells.

in cells of the endothelial or haemopoietic system. Those of mammals are mostly restricted to liver parenchyma. It is therefore conjectured that the former may have evolved from ancestors resembling *Karyolysus* and the latter from ancestors resembling *Hepatozoon*.

If this were true, then the avian and saurian malaria parasites would seem to merit a separate subfamily. (See Fig 5.) Yet current opinion is reluctant to accord them even the rank of a separate genus. It is thought better to recognize the Plasmodiidae, Haemoproteidae and Haemogregarinidae as representing three distinct levels or grades of organization without commitment to any particular theory regarding their evolutionary history. A classification of this kind is called grado-genetic, in contrast to the cladogenetic (or phylogenetic) type, which seeks to establish strictly monophyletic groups.[2] Another example of an evolutionary grade, of interest in the present context, is afforded by the Old and New World monkeys. These are considered, on fossil evidence, to have evolved independently from quite different prosimian stocks. Yet it is still customary to group them together as 'monkeys' by reason of the many convergent characters which they have in common.

Evolution of Vector-pathogen Systems: the Filarioid Nematodes

Although most filarioid nematodes have unknown vectors,[3] enough is known to suggest an extensive association with free-flying Diptera. All those known to parasitize man fall within this category. Before discussing their evolutionary relationships, therefore, something must be said about the evolution of bloodsucking in the Diptera.

Blood-feeding occurs sporadically in all three suborders of Diptera. In the Cyclorrhapha it is clearly a secondary development. The mandibles and maxillae are vestigial and the labium has been modified to form a piercing organ (Fig. 3a, p. 23). In those families of Brachycera with blood-feeding members (Tabanidae, Rhagionidae), as in blood-feeding Nematocera (Simuliidae, Ceratopogonidae, Psychodidae, Culicidae), the piercing organ is formed from the elongated mandibles and maxillae and the labium serves only as a protective sheath. The similarities between the mouthparts of all blood-feeding members of the two suborders are such as strongly to suggest that mouthparts of this kind had already evolved prior to the final differentiation of the Brachycera and Nematocera.

Almost the entire range of blood-feeding arthropods in involved in the transmission of filarioids having infective stages in the blood, though mosquitoes seem to predominate.[3] As against this, only pool-feeding Diptera and some other non-flying vectors with comparable modes of feeding can transmit those filarioids having infective stages in the dermis and sub-epidermis. Among Cyclorrhapha only the highly specialized hippoboscids are known to transmit filarioids with infective stages in the blood, though some wound-feeding muscids are vectors of *Parafilaria*. (See below.) These relations are basic to our present ideas regarding filarioid evolution.

Arthropod-borne filarioids differ from malaria parasites and their relatives in being wholly extracellular at all stages of their development. Entry into the vertebrate is not by injection but by active burrowing, usually, it would seem, through the incision made by the vector. The only feature common to the evolution of the two types of system seems to have been the original establishment in the vertebrate gut. Infection of the vector is by the uptake of prematurely hatching, incompletely differentiated pre-larvae (microfilariae). In some cases these retain the stretched egg-shell as a flexible sheath. They accumulate in the peripheral blood-vessels or superficial layers of the skin. The adult worms are found in various deeper tissues. They show no special association with the gut, but it is generally thought that they originated from rhabditine nematodes ingested by mouth.[1,4] Some present-day rhabditines are facultative parasites. Others have alternate free-living and parasitic generations, the former being rhabditoid and the latter filarioid in general morphology. Entry into the host takes place in the third larval stage. This has remained true throughout the evolution of the filarioids right up to the level of the mosquito-borne forms, in which almost all contact with the external environment has been lost.

A simplified classification of the filarioid nematodes and their relatives is shown in Fig. 6.

A major event in the evolution of the group seems to have been the establishment of the Ascaridoidea as intestinal and the Spiruroidea as stomach parasites. This allowed forward migration of the latter, via the oesophagus, and the establishment of ancestral forms, resembling primitive present-day thelaziids, in the orbit. Subsequent establishment of the adult worms in subcutaneous tissues may have taken place either through the agency of eye-feeding and wound-feeding Diptera or more probably, by migration.[4] This is thought to have been followed by piercing of the skin by the female worm and deposition of eggs or infective larvae in bleeding skin lesions as in *Parafilaria* (Filariidae). Here they are exposed to blood-feeding muscids which serve as vectors.

Pool-feeding Brachycera and Nematocera may have entered the

c

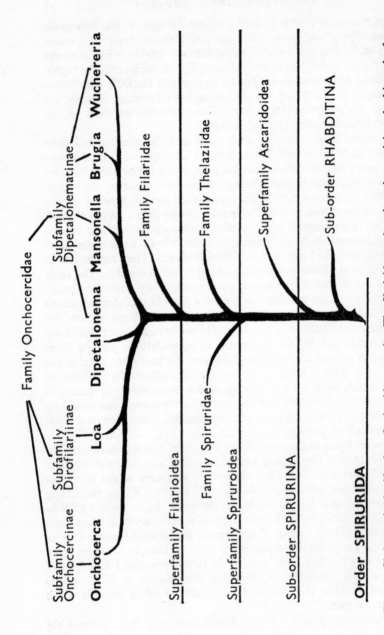

Fig. 6. Cladogenetic classification of spirurid nematodes. The filarioids are thought to have originated, ultimately, from free-living rhabditines which became established in the vertebrate gut. After this their evolution must have followed an entirely different course from that of the malaria parasites.

Family Onchocercidae

Subfamily Dipetalonematinae

Wuchereria

Brugia

Mansonella

Dipetalonema

Loa

Subfamily Dirofilariinae

Onchocerca

Subfamily Onchocercinae

Family Filariidae

Family Thelaziidae

Superfamily Ascaridoidea

Sub-order RHABDITINA

Superfamily Filarioidea

Family Spiruridae

Superfamily Spiruroidea

Sub-order SPIRURINA

Order SPIRURIDA

picture at this point, but they probably only became important with the spreading of the filarioid larvae into the dermis and sub-epidermis. The final stage was reached with the entry of infective pre-larvae into the blood and the freeing of the adult worm from dependence on superficial tissues. A further refinement seems to have been added independently by those Dirofilariinae and Dipetalonematinae (*Dirofilaria, Loa, Brugia, Wuchereria*) in which the concentration of microfilariae in the peripheral blood assumes a periodicity matching the twenty-four-hour feeding rhythm of the vector.

Evolution of Arthropod-borne Viruses

The number of known arthropod-borne animal viruses (arboviruses) has approximately trebled in the last ten years. More than two hundred are currently known. Only about half of them have known vectors but the others can be confidently ascribed to the arbovirus group on the basis of their ability to multiply in arthropod, as well as vertebrate, tissues and the possession of characteristic biochemical properties. Further confirmation is provided, in many cases, by the demonstration of their serological affinities with other viruses known to be transmitted by arthropods. These affinities form the basis of their classification.[5]

About eighty of those arboviruses with known vectors are transmitted by mosquitoes, twenty by ticks and a half-dozen or so by ceratopogonids or psychodids (Phlebotomini). Those which have been recovered from mosquitoes and are known to be capable of infecting man under natural conditions are listed in Table 1 together with the taxonomic groups to which they are assigned. These groups were formerly distinguished by letters of the alphabet but, as they grew in number, it was decided instead to designate them by the name of one of the members.

Most textbooks of parasitology omit bacteria and viruses, consigning these to a separate discipline, microbiology. Some justify this by reference to their special characteristics, others simply on grounds of convenience. Some would even argue that viruses cannot be properly considered as living organisms at all. From the ecological point of view this is hard to accept. As we shall see, every arbovirus that has been adequately studied proves to have its own distinctive ecology.[6] The role of these viruses in disease systems is one of parasitism by all the criteria adduced above. There is no indication that the factors governing their evolution have differed in principle from those governing the evolution of other kinds of parasites.

TABLE I

Mosquito-borne viruses known to infect man

Group A		Group C	Caraparu
	Chikungunya		Murutucu
	Eastern equine		Oriboca
	Mayaro		Restan
	Middleburg		
	Onyongnyong	Bunyamwera	Bunyamwera
	Semliki Forest	Group	Germiston
	Sindbis		Guaroa
	Venezuelan equine		Wyeomyia
	Western equine		
Group B			
	Dengue 1	Bwamba	Bwamba
	Dengue 2	Group	Pongola
	Dengue 3		
	Dengue 4	California	California
	Ilheus	Group	
	Japanese B		
	Kokobera	Guama	Catu
	Kunfin	Group	Guama
	Murray Valley		
	SAH 336		
	St Louis	Simbu	Oropouche
	Spondweni	Group	Simbu
	Uganda S		
	Wesselsbron		
	West Nile	Ungrouped	Mapputta
	Yellow fever		Rift Valley
	Zika		Tahyna
			Witwatersrand

Theories regarding the origin of viruses fall into three main groups, those deriving them direct from the primitive soup, those which regard them as cell components which have achieved a measure of independence and those which derive them by degeneration from more complex organisms (bacteria, rickettsias). The last of these is of special ecological interest in relation to the arboviruses. Some hundreds of species of bacteria have been recorded from arthropods and a variety of pathogenic forms are said to be transmitted casually in nature. Yet only four systems are known which involve regular transmission by blood-feeding arthropods. These are plague, tularaemia, brucellosis and melioidosis. One of them (plague) involves the destruction of the vector and all are independent of transmission by arthropods and can be disseminated by other means. The vectors in all cases are wingless (fleas, ticks).

Rickettsias are now generally accepted, on biochemical grounds, as degenerate bacteria. Their vector relations are more satisfactory than those of the bacteria but they, also, are confined to wingless vectors (ticks, mites, fleas, lice). In contrast to this, as we have seen, the very great majority of those arboviruses of which we have knowledge are transmitted by free-flying vectors. It thus seems a feasible hypothesis that bacteria and rickettsias impose too great a load on free-flying vectors and that the arboviruses may have evolved from these by a process of simplification (possibly involving the loss of the DNA component since all those arboviruses which have been investigated possess RNA only).

In our present state of knowlege we can speculate only in very general terms regarding the evolution of arbovirus systems. It has been suggested that tick-borne systems may be the most primitive. This would contradict the hypothesis outlined above. The indications may rather be that tick-borne systems originated secondarily under climatic conditions too stringent for vectors less closely associated with their hosts. The Russian spring-summer complex of tick-borne viruses might conceivably be an example. The small number of arboviruses known to be transmitted by sandflies (Phlebotomini) or ceratopogonids are, perhaps, more promising. In this connection we may note the apparent association, in both the malaria parasites and the filarioids, of the most highly evolved parasites with mosquito vectors. This is especially noticeable in the case of the malaria parasites, plasmodiids being associated, so far as is known, exclusively with mosquitoes and haemoproteids exclusively with pool-feeding Diptera.

Evidence from vertebrate hosts is equally tenuous. Arboviruses with cold-blooded hosts have only quite recently come to light and we still know very little about them or their vectors. It is possibly significant that in systems involving both birds and mammals the primary hosts are birds but the only systems of the kind so far studied are those involving man and domestic animals as the mammalian hosts, which are clearly artificial.

Evidence may come from the viruses themselves. The present classification of arboviruses is essentially phylogenetic, since it is based on the supposed evolutionary divergence of antigens originally held in common. If convergence is ruled out, it can be argued that the member of any group possessing most antigens in common with other members of the group is the most likely to be primitive. It has, for example, been suggested, on evidence of this kind, that West Nile is the most primitive of the Group B viruses. Further analyses of this kind could be very useful and suggestive to the ecologist.

The Involvement of Man

In this chapter we have dealt mainly with pathogens and their relations with their vectors. There remains for consideration the question of the involvement of man and other vertebrate hosts in the course of evolution. Before we can deal with this adequately it will be necessary to describe in more detail the life-histories of the various pathogens. This will be the subject of the next chapter.

REFERENCES

1. TAYLOR, A. E. R., (Ed.), 1965, *Evolution of Parasites*. Oxford: Blackwell.
2. CAIN, A. J. (Ed.), 1959, *Function and Taxonomic Importance*. London: Systematics Association.
3. TAYLOR, A. E. R., (Ed.), 1964, *Host-parasite Relations in Invertebrate Hosts*. Oxford: Blackwell.
4. ANDERSON, R. C., 1957, The life cycles of dipetalonematid nematodes (Filarioidea, Dipetalonematidae): the problem of their evolution'. *J. Helminth.*, **31**: 203-224.
5. CASALS, J., 1967, 'Immunological techniques for animal viruses'. *in* Maramorosch, K. & Koprowski, H. (Eds.). *Methods in Virology*. III. New York & London: Academic Press.
6. DARLINGTON, C. D., MATTINGLY, P. F. & SMITH, C. E. G., 1960, 'Symposium on the evolution of arborvirus diseases'. *Trans. R. Soc. trop. Med. Hyg.*, **54**: 89-134.

III

Life-histories of Mosquito-borne Pathogens

Human Malaria Parasites

THE term 'malaria parasite' is used in different senses by different authors. Some confine it to the genus *Plasmodium*. Others include *Haemoproteus*. Still others include the whole of the Haemosporina (Fig. 5, p. 31). We shall restrict the term 'malaria' to infections with *Plasmodium*. The four different species of human malaria parasite cause four different diseases. *Plasmodium malariae* causes quartan malaria. *P. vivax* causes benign tertian. *P. ovale* causes ovale malaria. *P. falciparum* causes malignant tertian. Thus 'malaria', used collectively, is a purely colloquial term. In any context demanding precision it requires to be qualified according to the particular parasite concerned.

P. *falciparum* and its relative *P. reichenowi* of chimpanzees and gorillas are sufficiently distinct to be placed in a separate subgenus, *Laverania*. The other kinds of human malaria parasites are also all represented by related forms in apes and monkeys. Some of these are capable of establishment in man. Recent cases of natural and accidental infection of man with monkey parasites have been reported. Simian malaria is consequently now regarded as a zoonosis. We shall have more to say about it later. Fig. 7 shows a generalized life-cycle applicable in broad outline to all the species of *Plasmodium* normally found in man. By convention man is regarded as the intermediate, and the mosquito as the definitive host, since it is in the latter that fusion of gametes takes place.

It was believed for a long time that injection of sporozoites by the mosquito was followed immediately by their entry into circulating erythrocytes. There remained, however, an unaccountably long interval between the infective bite and the appearance of detectable parasites. Analogy with avian malaria suggested that pre-erythrocytic development might take place in endothelial cells, but this proved not

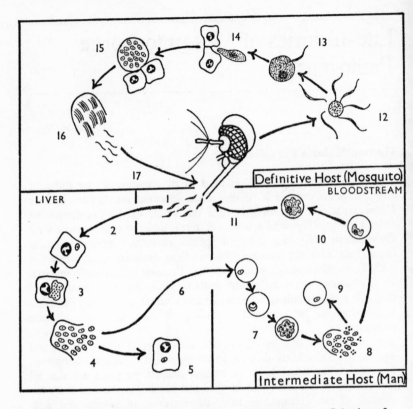

Fig. 7 Generalized life-cycle of human malaria parasite. 1 Injection of infective sporozoites into bloodstream. 2 Passage to liver. 3 Primary exoerythrocytic schizogony in liver. 4 Discharge of merozoites from liver cell. 5 Initiation of second exoerythrocytic cycle. 6 Entry into erythrocytes and initiation of first erythrocytic cycle. 7 Erythrocytic schizogony. 8 Discharge of merozoites and pigment into bloodstream. 9 Initiation of second erythrocytic cycle. 10 Maturation of gametocytes. 11 Uptake of mature gametocytes. 12 Exflagellation of microgametes. 13 Fertilization. 14 Penetration of gut wall by ookinete. 15 Maturation of oocyst and sporogony. 16 Discharge of sporozoites. 17 Passage of sporozoites to salivary glands.

to be the case. Eventually, in 1948, following experiments with monkeys, pre-erythrocytic schizonts were located, in human biopsy material, in the liver parenchyma. Young trophozoites first appear in circulating red blood-cells some days (in certain cases weeks or months) after the initial infection. These grow and divide to produce merozoites which are discharged, together with pigment formed by degradation of haemoglobin, by rupture of the erythrocytes.

The characteristic malarial paroxysm (chill [rigor], followed by fever, sweating and return to normal or subnormal temperature until the next bout) is thought to be an anaphylactic response to substances discharged with the merozoites. In well established, untreated infections schizogony is synchronous. It is this which is responsible for the quartan or tertain (four- or three-day) periodicity of symptoms (one day with fever, one or two days without, a third or fourth day with fever again). Asexual reproduction may persist for months or even years, the erythrocytic cycle being supported to an extent which varies with the parasite (greatest in *P. malariae*, least in *P. falciparum*) by repeated exoerythrocytic cycles in the liver.

Not all the merozoites produced by erythrocytic schizogony develop into schizonts. For reasons which are not understood a proportion develop into male and female gametocytes. Direct production of gametocytes by paraerythrocytic liver schizonts has also been suspected, though not proved. Uptake of gametocytes by a suitable species of anopheline mosquito is followed by the throwing off of flagelliform microgametes by the male gametocyte (exflagellation). Fertilization of the female gamete follows and the resultant zygote (ookinete) penetrates the stomach wall and becomes established as an oocyst on the outher surface below the epithelium. The reduction division, in *P. vivax*, the only human parasite studied, takes place during maturation of the oocyst. Division of the contents of the oocyst (sporogony) leads to the production of numerous fusiform sporozoites. These escape into the body cavity, by rupture of the oocyst, and pass forward to the salivary glands from which they are injected into the vertebrate host during the blood-meal.

During its residence in the mosquito the parasite is partially exposed to the influence of the external environment, particularly temperature. Table 2 (from Ref. 3 on p. 38) shows the effect of temperature on duration of sporogony.

Completion of erythrocytic schizogony takes approximately forty-eight hours in all the species except *P. malariae*, giving a tertian periodicity. In *P. falciparum*, however, the periodicity is frequently masked by uncontrolled schizogony. Consequently the type of malaria produced by this species is often called subtertian. *P. falciparum* also differs from the other species in that erythrocytic schizogony normally takes place mainly in the deeper vessels, so that only immature trophozoites (ring stages) and gametocytes are found in the peripheral circulation. Erythrocytes containing older trophozoites tend to clump together and may block the capillaries by adhering to their walls. This is one reason for the greater 'malignancy' of this type of malaria. As against this, relapses are much less frequent than with the other species owing mainly to the very restricted exoerythrocytic schizogony.

TABLE 2

Duration of sporogony at various temperatures

	30°C	24°C	20°C
P. vivax	7 days	9 days	16 days
P. falciparum	9 days	11 days	20 days
P. malariae	15 days	21 days	30 days
P. ovale		15days at 26°C	

After Garnham

Space will not permit any more detailed discussion of the differences between the species infecting man. For these reference should be made to the specialist literature.[1] A good general account will also be found in Ref. 2 on page 28.

Simian Malaria[2]

The experimental transmission of monkey malaria to man was first achieved more than thirty years ago. The parasite concerned, *P. knowlesi,* was later successfully employed for the treatment of neurosyphilis by malaria shock therapy. Despite this, litttle interest in the possibility of natural infection was aroused until, in 1960, two institutes in the United States reported accidental infections of laboratory workers by mosquitoes fed on infected monkeys. The parasite, in both cases, was *P. bastianelli,* usually considered a subspecies of *P. cynomolgi.* Subsequent investigations led to the demonstration of two infections of man acquired in the field, one, with *P. knowlesi,* in South-east Asia, the other, it is claimed, with *P. simium,* in Brazil.

Other investigations have so far yielded negative results and it is provisionally concluded that ecological situations in which man, monkey and appropriate vector make sufficiently close contact are likely to be restricted and to offer no great threat to the eradication of human malaria. Paradoxically the chief threat would seem to come from plasmodia of monkeys rather than anthropoids. As Table 3 shows, chimpanzees are the only anthropoids harbouring malaria parasites known to be transmissible to man and contact between these and potential human hosts is very limited.

TABLE 3

Simian malaria parasites transmissible to man

Human homologue	Simian parasites	Natural host(s)	Natural vector(s)	Mode of transmission to man
P. malariae	*P. rodhaini*	Chimpanzee	—	B
	P. brasilianum	Cebid monkeys	—	E
	P. inui	Macaques, etc.	*An. leucosphyrus* *An. hackeri* *An. balabacensis*	E
	(= *P. shortti*)			
P. vivax	*P. schwetzi*	Chimpanzee	—	E
	P. cynomolgi complex	Macaques, etc.	*An. leucosphyrus* *An. hackeri* *An. balabacensis* ssp. *introlatus*	E
P. ovale	*P. simium*	Howler monkey	*An. cruzi*	N*
—	*P. knowlesi*	Macaques, etc.	*An. hackeri*	EN

B. By blood inoculation; E. Experimentally by mosquito; N. Natural.

*See text.

It will be seen that Table 3 makes no mention of *P. falciparum*. The only generally accepted homologue of this parasite is *P. reichenowi* of chimpanzees and gorillas, which has so far resisted transfer to man or other hosts. *P. falciparum* will develop in chimpanzees though only to the pre-erythrocytic stage in those with intact spleens. It develops surprisingly well in splenectomized gibbons and some strains produce a low-grade infection in gibbons with intact spleens. The two laboratory infections of man with *P. cynomolgi bastianelli,* mentioned on p. 42, are listed in the table as experimental infections though unpremeditated. The infection of man with *P. simium,* though listed as natural, in fact involved a mosquito collector stationed on a platform in the forest canopy. The identity of the parasite has been questioned by some authors. *P. knowlesi,* long employed in the treatment of neurosyphilis and recently acquired as a natural infection by a visitor to Malaya, has a quotidian (one-day) periodicity and is without any homologue among the species normally found in man.

For further details regarding this very interesting group of parasites the reader should consult Refs. 1, 2 and 3 on p. 53.

Other Malaria parasites [3]

For reasons of expense avian plasmodia, particularly *P. cathemerium, P. relictum, P. gallinaceum* and *P. lophurae,* were long preferred as laboratory animals to those of apes and monkeys. More recently further possibilities have been opened up by the discovery of a plasmodium, *P. berghei,* of African forest tree rats (*Thamnomys*), which, with its allies *P. chabaudi* and *P. vinckei,* also from Africa, can be cultured in laboratory rodents. These, together with plasmodia of bats and ungulates, are currently placed in a separate subgenus, *Vinckeia.* Besides their value for experimental purposes, and intrinsic biological interest, they pose an important problem for the epidemiologist. It can no longer be considered safe to base assessments of vector status purely on sporozoite counts. Rodent malaria parasites have been used extensively in the study of immunological and other responses to infection on the part of the vertebrate host. For this the reader should consult the specialist literature.[4]

Human Filarioid Nematodes

Only two mosquito-borne species infecting man have been identified with certainty though the existence of others is suspected. The species in question are *Wuchereria bancrofti* and *Brugia malayi.* Their systematic position in relation to other Onchocercidae infecting man, but with different vectors, is shown in Fig. 6 (p. 34). Among the latter *Onchocerca volvula,* transmitted by *Simulium* spp, is located, in the adult stage, in subcutaneous tissues. The pre-larvae (microfilariae) are not found in the bloodstream. In all these respects *Onchocerca* is thought to be more primitive than the mosquito-borne genera (see p. 32). The microfilariae have an affinity for the optic nerve and can cause blindness. *O. volvula* has been found in a Mexican monkey and in a gorilla. A chimpanzee has been successfully infected artificially. Other species of the genus occur in wild and domestic ungulates.

Loa loa resembles the mosquito-borne genera in the occurrence of the microfilariae in the bloodstream and their retention of the stretched egg-shell as a sheath (Fig. 8). Concentration in the peripheral blood, in both groups, exhibits a periodicity matching the biting rhythm of the vectors (in this case diurnal tabanids). The young adults wander actively about the body, below the skin, and are not infrequently seen crossing the eye. The very closely related form found in African gorillas, baboons and forest monkeys may or may not be conspecific.

Two species of *Dipetalonema, D. perstans* and *D. streptocerca*, parasitize man. The microfilariae are aperiodic and unsheathed. They are found in the blood. The vectors are ceratopogonids (*Culicoides* spp.). Other species have been shown to develop in mosquitoes, fleas, lice, ticks and hippoboscids. Hosts include rodents and carnivores.

Mansonella ozzardi resembles *D. perstans*. It is transmitted by *Simulium* and *Culicoides* and is known only from man. Other members of the family, widely used for experimental purposes, include *Dirofilaria immitis* of the dog, transmitted by mosquitoes, and *Litomosoides carinii*, of rodents, transmitted by mites.

Aside from the periodicity of the microfilariae, the life-histories of all forms of *Brugia* and *Wuchereria* are similar and Fig. 8 will serve for all. Infective larvae leave the proboscis on contact with the warm skin. A proportion penetrate the skin by way of the puncture made by the mouth-parts. No host other than man is available and consequently the time taken for maturation of the adults is unknown. There are indications that it is longer than for *B. malayi* which take about ten-fifteen weeks in cats.[5] The adults are found mainly in lymph glands and lymphatics. They are slender, threadlike and up to 10 cm. long in the temale, 5 cm in the male. This compares with a maximum of about 2 mm for the infective larvae. The females may live for several years and, during that time, produce very numerous, minute microfilariae.

W. bancrofti and *B. malayi* occur in both periodic and subperiodic forms.[5] In the periodic forms the microfilariae concentrate in the vessels of the lung for most of the twenty-four hours, appearing in the peripheral circulation mainly during the middle part of the night. In

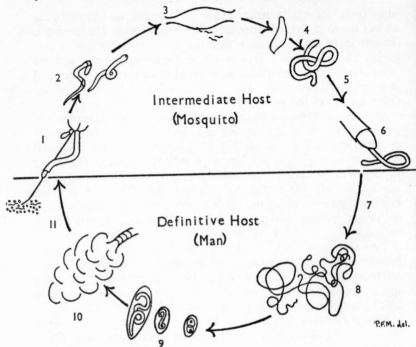

Fig. 8 Life-history of the nocturnally periodic form of *Wuchereria bancrofti*. 1 Uptake of microfilariae from peripheral blood. 2 Exsheathment. 3 Penetration of wall of mosquito gut. 4 Maturation of larvae in thoracic muscles. 5 Migration of infective larvae to proboscis. 6 Deposition of infective larvae on skin. 7 Metamorphosis to adult in lymphatics. 8 Mature male and female in permanent association. 9 Development of microfilariae in utero. 10 Microfilariae concentrated in lung during daytime. 11. Nocturnal migration to peripheral blood.

the subperiodic forms the nocturnal peak is suppressed and there is a more uniform distribution over the twenty-four hours, though still with a tendency to concentration in the peripheral blood when the vector is normally most active (Fig. 9).

Shortly after ingestion by the mosquito the microfilarial sheaths are ruptured. The young larvae, thus liberated, pierce the gut wall by means of a stylet. From the haemocoel they migrate to the thoracic muscles where they shorten and thicken, assuming a characteristic 'sausage' shape. Maturation takes about a fortnight and involves two

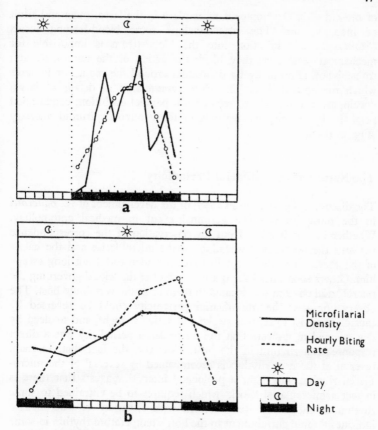

Fig. 9 Correlation between microfilarial periodicity and biting rhythm of vector. **a** Nocturnally periodic *Wuchereria bancrofti* and *Culex pipiens fatigans*. **b** Subperiodic *W. bancrofti* and *Aedes polynesiensis*.

moults. When it is complete the infective third-stage larvae, now more than twenty times the size of the original microfilariae, pass forward into the proboscis.

These details of development in the vector are paralleled with remarkable fidelity in certain thelaziids (*Draschia*, *Habronema*) parasitizing horses. They are, however, purely gut parasites in the vertebrate host. The pre-larvae hatch prematurely in the gut and are passed out in the droppings to be ingested by the dung-feeding larvae of muscid flies. Development takes place in the larva, pupa and adult of these vectors. The latter include some blood-feeding forms (*Stomoxys*), but injection into the bloodstream is impossible for mechanical reasons as they block the action of the mouthpart and transmission is normally by deposition around the mouth or in sores which the animal licks. The close resemblance in details of larval development is thought to result from parallel evolution, conditioned pershaps by preadaptive features in the common spiruroid ancestry (Fig. 6, p. 34).

The Nature of Microfilarial Periodicity

The discovery, by Manson in 1877, of the development of *W. bancrofti* in the mosquito was the germinal event in medical entomology. Whether or not it arose from his observation of the correspondence between the nocturnal 'swarming' of the microfilariae and the habits of the vector, it is clear that this correspondence did not long escape him. Others soon raised the question whether the 'clock' governing the microfilarial rhythm was located in them or in the vertebrate host. The observation that the microfilarial periodicity could be reversed by causing the host to remain awake and active at night, and to sleep by day, seemed to indicate that the microfilarial periodicity was a direct response to a rhythm in the host. However, the fact that, in man, reversal of the host rhythm is accompanied by reversal of the micro-filarial rhythm only after a prolonged interval suggests that there is in fact a microfilarial 'clock' which requires to be entrained to some rhythm in the host.[6] Recent work with a variety of microfilariae indicates a rapid entrainment to the host's temperature rhythm in some genera and species and an independence of this rhythm in others, among them *Brugia* and *Wuchereria*.[7]

The periodic form of *W. bancrofti* is distributed throughout the tropics, except in the Pacific area where it is replaced by the sub-periodic form (Fig. 13a, p. 62). The latter has very much the appear-ance of a parasite introduced by man which has become adapted to new vectors. Its principal vectors are *Aedes* spp., notably members of the *Ae scutellaris* complex (p. 78). Those of the periodic form are various *Anopheles* spp. and *C. p. fatigans*. Subperiodic *B. malayi*, unlike either form of *W. bancrofti*, is found in a wide variety of forest animals (p. 61) and can be easily transmitted to laboratory hosts. Very interestingly it remains subperiodic when transferred from man to domestic cats, assumes a nocturnal periodicity when passed from cats to monkeys and reverts to subperiodicity when transferred from leaf monkey to cat. We still have much to learn regarding the physiology of these rhythms. One thing, however, seems certain. All evidence combines to suggest that the abandonment of the lung by the microfilariae and their subsequent passive transport to the peripheral blood-vessels is a classic example of migration, in the sense of the passage from a nutritively favourable to a nutritively less favourable site offering better chances of dispersal.

Development of Arboviruses in the Vector (Ref. 3, p. 38)

The essential qualification for inclusion among the arboviruses is the ability to multiply in both vertebrate and arthropod tissues. Such an ability does not necessarily imply transmission by an arthropod in nature. Many arboviruses still have no known vectors though it is a reasonable presumption that they exist. One, the Rio Bravo virus of bats, has no known vector and is known to be transmitted in the saliva. It is, nevertheless, on serological and biochemical evidence, a typical Group B virus closely related to St Louis.

Some mosquito-borne viruses can multiply in the tissues of a surprisingly wide range of arthropods. Both Group A and Group B viruses have been serially transmitted through several generations in grasshoppers, moths, beetles and ticks. More than this is required, however, for establishment in a particular vector. The prime requirement appears to be the ability to multiply in the wall of the mid-gut (Fig. 10). If this is bypassed by injection into the haemocoel the range of potential arthropod hosts becomes greatly extended.

Even when natural uptake alone is involved, the range of potential vectors is commonly greater than the range actually encountered in nature. Occasional recovery of virus from a particular vector does not necessarily imply that this vector is responsible for regular transmission. The factors which ultimately determine the importance of any particular vector are ecological. As an example, the concentration of virus in the peripheral blood varies widely as between different kinds of vertebrate host. So does the threshold of infectibility in different vectors (Table 4). Interplay between these two limiting factors may determine whether a given species is an efficient vector in a particular environment. Again, viruses in their arthropod vectors are subject to the effects of environmental temperature. This can greatly affect the time taken for an infected mosquito to become infective. The so-called extrinsic incubation period for yellow fever virus, in *Aedes aegypti*,

D

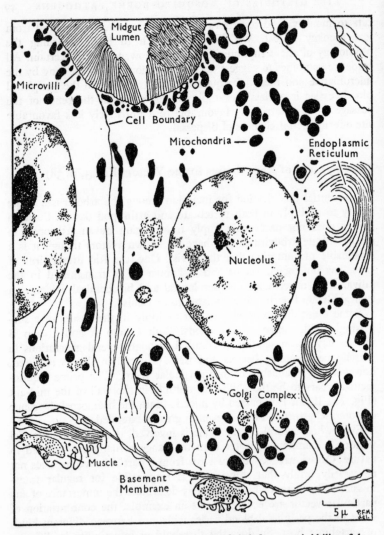

Fig. 10 Section of mid-gut epithelium of unfed *Aedes aegypti.* Ability of the virus to multiply in these cells appears to be a decisive element in the infectibility of the vector. Infection with Semliki Forest virus appears to have no effect on the extensive changes which accompany digestion of the blood-meal. Presumed virus particles can be detected in the salivary glands and mid-gut but they are relatively scanty and, in the case of the mid-gut, concentrated towards the cell wall, especially near the basement membrane. (After Bertram & Bird, *Trans. R. Soc. trop. Med. Hyg.*, **55**: 404, 1961.)

varies from thirty-six days at 18°C to four days at 37°C. This factor alone could be quite sufficient to determine whether a particular vector survived long enough to become infective. Wide differences also exist as between different vectors. Thus the extrinsic incubation period for the same virus in *Haemagogus spegazzinii* is twenty-one to twenty-two days at 24°-27°C as compared to about seven-eleven days over the same temperature range in *Ae. aegypti*. The effect is not simple. Increased temperature leads to a greater proportion of both mosquitoes becoming infected while mosquitoes kept at a constant temperature of, say, 25°C between infective more slowly than those kept at an average temperature of 25°C.

TABLE 4

Host and vector thresholds in Eastern equine Encephalomyelitis

Mosquito		Vertebrate				
		Virus titre reached in blood				
Species	Blood titre needed for infection	Cardinal 7·2–8·4	Grackle 6·3–7·4	White Ibis 3·5–5·3	American Egret 2·5–3·6	Horse 0·5–4·5
Ae. sollicitans	2·0–3·0	+	+	+	+	+
Ae. aegypti	3·0–4·5	+	+	+	+	+
Culis. melanura	4·5–5·5	+	+	+		
Ae. vexans	6·0–7·0	+	+			
Culex fatigans	7·5–8·5	+				

+ indicates that mosquito and vertebrate host appear capable of virus maintenance. After Schaeffer & Arnold, *Amer. J. Hyg.*, **60**: 231, 1954

After multiplying in the stomach wall the virus spreads to a variety of tissues with, it would seem, in general, a particular affinity for nervous tissue and salivary glands. Several arboviruses have been shown to persist through to the adult mosquito when administered in sufficient quantity to the larvae. Trans-stadial transmission of this kind is important in the tick-borne viruses though less likely to be of any importance in mosquitoes for obvious reasons. Trans-ovarian transmission also appears to have some importance in ticks (though its extent is disputed). There is no evidence for it in mosquitoes.

Arboviruses in their Vertebrate Hosts

Inoculation into a susceptible vertebrate host is followed, in general, by rapid multiplication and the appearance of a high concentration of virus in the blood within one-five days. Antibody is detectable ten days to a fortnight after inoculation and may persist for months or even years. Although most arboviruses are pantropic, i.e., capable of infecting a variety of vertebrate tissues, they frequently show an affinity for particular tissues and a corresponding association with particular sorts of pathological damage. Such associations do not necessarily reflect their systematic position. Thus highly neurotropic encephalitis viruses, associated with damage to the brain, are found both in Group A (Eastern, Western and Venezuelan encephalitis, see p. 36) and in Group B (St Louis encephalitis, Japanese B encephalitis). Some viruses (Chikungunya and Onyongnyong in Group A, West Nile

Fig. 11   Portion of a liver cell of an African monkey infected with yellow fever virus. There are numerous virus particles in the cytoplasm. The endoplasmic reticulum (e.r.) is greatly expanded and there is an extensive multiplication of mitochondria, presumed to be a protective reaction. This reaction is apparently peculiar to African primates and is not shown by Oriental or South American monkeys. (After Bearcroft, *J. Path. Bact.*, 83: 59, 1962. × 8,500.)

and the dengue complex in Group B) produce almost identical symptoms, notably severe pain in the back and joints. For a long time these symptoms were known collectively as 'dengue', which was regarded as a single disease. Now that we know that such symptoms can be produced by quite unrelated viruses the name has had to be restricted to the disease caused by one small group of closely related organisms.

Yellow fever is an example of a viscerotropic virus affecting various organs but especially the liver. Neurotropic strains can, however, be readily produced by serial passage in the brains of infant mice. This virus is highly lethal to Asian rhesus monkeys and to various kinds of South American monkeys. African monkeys, on the other hand, can tolerate heavy infections. In African guenons (*Cercopithecus*) and patas monkeys (*Erythrocebus*) multiplication of the virus in the liver is accompanied by a massive proliferation of mitochondria, serving, presumably, to offset the increased energy requirements resulting from multiplication of the virus (Fig. 11). It is thought that other African primates with a high degree of tolerance, including man, would show a similar response. If so, it would seem that we have here an interesting example of parallel evolution meriting further investigation.

REFERENCES

1. GARNHAM, P. C. C., 1966, *Malaria Parasites and Other Haemosporidia* Oxford: Blackwell.
2. BRUCE-CHWATT, L. J., 1968, 'Malaria zoonosis in relation to malaria eradication'. *Trop. geogr. Med.*, 20: 50-87
3. GARNHAM, P. C. C., 1967, 'Malaria in mammals excluding man'. *Adv. Parasit.* 5: 139-204.
4. ZUCKERMAN, A., in press, 'Immunological aspects of rodent malaria'. *in* Jackson, G. J. & Singer, I. (Eds.). *Immunity to Animal Parasites*. New York: Appleton-Century-Crufts.
5. EDESON, J. F. B. & WILSON, T., 1964, 'The epidemiology of filariasis due to *Wuchereria bancrofti* and *Brugia malayi*'. *A. Rev. Ent.*, 9: 245-268.
6. MATTINGLY, P. F., 1962, 'Some considerations relating to the role of *Culex pipiens fatigans* Wiedemann in the transmission of human filariases'. *Bull. Wld Hlth Org.*, 27: 569-578.
7. HAWKING, F., 1965, 'Advances in filariases, especially concerning periodicity of microfilariae.' *Trans. R. Soc. Med. Hyg.*, 59: 9-21.

IV

The Involvement of Man

SINCE the discovery of jungle yellow fever, in the 1930s, new mosquito-borne zoonoses have continually come to light. Interest in the ecology of such diseases has grown correspondingly. With the general growth of interest in primatology and its implications for human biology has come an increased awareness of the importance of the evolutionary background in shaping mosquito-borne diseases as we know them today.

Origins of Primate Malaria

Various species of saurian *Plasmodium* occur in both Old and New World lizards. It is possible, therefore, that this genus had already differentiated before the end of the Mesozoic. Fossil simians are known from the Oligocene and it has even been suggested, on recent evidence, that recognizable pongid and hominid stocks may have diverged before the end of the Eocene. Something deserving the name of simian malaria may therefore have existed quite early in the Tertiary (Fig. 12).

The occurrence of *P. brasilianum* in New World monkeys has been held to suggest an Eocene origin for the quartan group of parasites. Fossil evidence suggests, however, that the New and Old World monkeys originated from quite distinct prosimian stocks, their resemblances being due largely to convergence.[1] Other evidence contraindicative of the existence of simian or prosimian malaria, in both hemispheres, at so early a date is the absence from the New World of any species of *Hepatocystis* and of any mammalian *Plasmodium* other than those of man and monkeys. In view of these facts the hypothesis that *P. brasilianum* has been acquired from man by South American monkeys seems distinctly more plausible. It has recently been shown that several South American monkeys (*Aotus, Saguinus, Saimiri*) are susceptible to infection with *P. vivax*. Night monkeys (*Aotus*), in

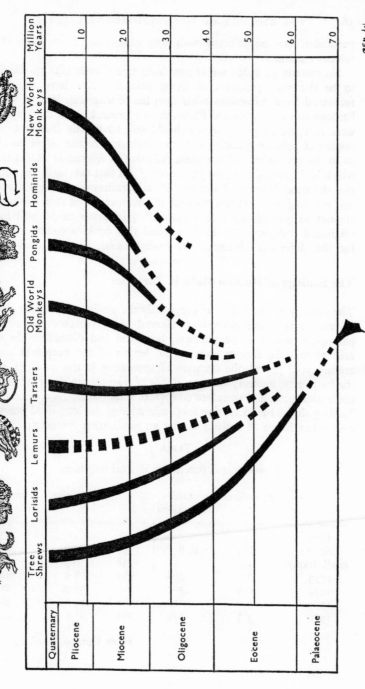

Fig. 12 Outline scheme of primate evolution. Although the first appearance of a recognizable hominid, as opposed to simian, stock is generally thought to have taken place in the Oligocene, there is some recent evidence to suggest that the divergence may have taken place still earlier. Old and New World monkeys seem to have originated from quite distinct prosimian stocks and to owe most of their resemblances to convergence.

		Million Years
Quaternary		
Pliocene		1 0
Miocene		2 0
Oligocene		3 0
		4 0
Eocene		5 0
		6 0
Palaeocene		7 0

Tree Shrews Lorisids Lemurs Tarsiers Old World Monkeys Pongids Hominids New World Monkeys

P.F.M. del.

particular, can be infected with surprising ease, even when their spleens are intact.

No malaria parasites are known from tree shrews (Pl. 1), thought to be the most primitive of living primates. Nor have any been recovered from prosimians other than the Madagascan lemurs, which harbour two poorly studied *Plasmodium* species. Even if these species were accepted as primitive we should still have little clue as to the origins of primate malaria, since the geological record offers no clue as to the provenance of the great radiation of lemurs in Madagascar which took place during the Pleistocene.[2] All that can really be said is that the wide diversity of simian malaria parasites occurring in Southeast Asia suggests that this has been the main centre of their evolution, at least in geologically recent times. *P. falciparum* might well have originated independently in Africa and this could account, in part, for the differences between *Plasmodium* s.str. and *Laverania*.

The Ecology of Human Malaria Parasites

The ecology of the vector, as supposedly the weakest link in the chain of transmission, has often been allowed to overshadow that of the pathogens, which is, nevertheless, both real and distinctive. In the case of malaria, factors such as the length of the prepatent (pre-erythrocytic) period, the duration of sporogony in the mosquito and the frequency, intensity and persistence of relapses are clearly of major epidemiological, and therefore ecological, importance. As an example, Table 5 shows the increasing preponderance of the long-lived quartan over other forms of malaria during an eradication campaign.

TABLE 5

P. malariae as percentage of total infections

	P. malariae %	total infections		*P. malariae* %	total infections
1949 (before eradication)	0·4	49 927	1957	2·7	146
			1958	0·5	738
1953	0·7	268	1959	8·0	184
1954	0·5	361	1960	35·0	83
1955	0·9	222	1961	79·0	28
1956	3·3	179	1962	95·0	23

From Garnham, ref. 1, p. 53

This long persistence of *P. malariae* may, it is suggested, render it particularly suited to maintenance in small host populations or where there is only sporadic contact with the vector. It might be imagined to be better suited than other species to maintenance among the small hunting groups of early man. Human quartan malaria formerly extended as far north in the Old World as Great Britain and the Netherlands. The related *P. inui* is the most widely distributed of any of the simian parasites. It has been recorded as far north and west as West Pakistan. Surprisingly, no quartan parasite is known from African monkeys, even from baboons, which are closely related to the Asian macaques. The latter appear to have extended into western Europe in Pleistocene times, the Barbary ape being a relict.

P. falciparum was until recently the cause of widespread and highly lethal malaria in southern Europe. It was responsible for severe epidemics as far north as Archangel (61° 30′ N).[3] It has ben recorded from above 8,000 feet in Africa and above 9,000 feet in the southern USSR.

For most of the stable, endemic malaria in northern latitudes, however, we must look to *P. vivax*, of all the human malaria parasites the best adapted to maintenance in cold climates. This parasite was formerly established as far north as Scandinavia in the west and Siberia in the east. After about the middle of the nineteenth century it began to retreat southwards, largely, it is believed, because of improved methods of agriculture involving the reclamation of marshland and the stabling of cattle which provided concentrated alternative host populations for the vector. Improvements in domestic lighting and hygiene may also have assisted by reducing the numbers of vectors hibernating in houses. Endemic malaria had disappeared from Great Britain and much of north-west Europe by the turn of the century. Apart from fortuitous introductions and accidental infections, the whole of continental Europe is said to have been free of malaria throughout 1967.

Strains of *P. vivax* from different parts of its range show marked differences in the length of the prepatent period. In *P. vivax hibernans*, from Siberia and other northerly parts of the Soviet Union, prior to eradication, this was as long as 253-381 days, an evident adaptation to restricted seasonal transmission. Russian workers have suggested that *P. vivax* originated from *P. cynomolgi bastianelli*, acquired by man as a zoonosis in South-east Asia and transported by him to more northerly latitudes. This, if true, would suggest a comparatively recent introduction of *P. vivax* into Africa, possibly from more temperate latitudes to the north, and would be consistent with the decline in its incidence in tropical latitudes in that continent. West African Negro (as opposed to Bantu) peoples show a remarkable immunity to *vivax* malaria, maintained even in the descendants of slaves brought to the New World some centuries ago. This could be taken to suggest a prolonged experience of, and adaptation to, the parasite. Alternatively it could betoken a comparatively recent contact and a failure of the parasite, as yet, to adapt to West African Negroes.

Plasmodium ovale contrasts sharply with *P. vivax* in nearly all the salient features mentioned. Whereas *P. vivax* and the related *P. cynomolgi* are highly polymorphic species, *P. ovale* shows little variation throughout its range. Whereas *P. vivax* is largely absent from West Africa, *P. ovale* attains its greatest frequency there, particularly in the more humid wooded and forested areas. It is possible that its distribution reflects an association with the more primitive forest-dwelling peoples confined to this part of Africa by the westward movement of the Bantu. Such a hypothesis would also be consistent with its very restricted distribution outside Africa, where it is known for certain only from the Philippines and New Guinea – two of the very few remaining refuges of primitive forest-dwelling Negritos.[4] The relationships of *P. ovale* are disputed. It has been compared to certain South-east Asian monkey parasites. More recently, on the other hand, it has been argued persuasively that it is a form of *P. schwetzi* acquired as a zoonosis from African apes. The possibility that *P. simium* was acquired in the reverse direction from man seems worth considering (p. 54).

Entry of Malaria into the New World

There is general agreement that human malaria originated in the Old World and was carried to the New World by man. Argument centres chiefly on the question whether the introduction took place before or after the time of Columbus. Two possible modes of pre-Columbian introduction have been envisaged. The first is by early man across the Bering Strait. The second is by trans-Pacific voyagers who may have brought it to the west coast of South America from eastern Asia or Melanesia.[5] There are cultural resemblances strongly suggestive of contact in prehistoric times and indications that malaria was formerly more highly endemic in western coastal areas than elsewhere in South America. Malaria is absent from Polynesia and Micronesia, where there are no anopheline mosquitoes, apart from a wartime introduction into Guam, but an introduction from the other areas does not seem wholly impossible.

Introduction into North America, via the Bering bridge, is usually ruled out on account of the cold. This seems, however, to be a considerable oversimplification. It is estimated that, at the present time, summer temperatures in eastern Siberia are sufficient to permit transmission up to 62°N or in warm years 64°N, which is about the southern limit of the Bering Straits. The area has a stable, continental type of climate but, even so, these limits would lie a degree or so further north still at the time of the postglacial optimum (about 4,000 BC). Anopheline mosquitoes have been found as far north as 64°N in central Alaska and malaria has been recorded from British Columbia. While, therefore, admitting the intrinsic improbability of an introduction of malaria by this route, the question seems to deserve a more thorough examination than it has so far received, particularly with regard to the possible access of nomadic peoples to areas of stable malaria and bearing in mind the remarkable proclivities of *P. vivax hibernans*.

Falciparum Malaria and the Sickle-cell Gene

Several human genetically based abnormalities (thalassaemia, glucose-6-phosphate-dehydrogenase deficiency, sickle-cell anaemia) have been thought to be protective against severe malaria. The case seems best established for the sickle-cell gene and with specific reference to *falciparum* malaria. About 80 per cent of children homozygous for the sickle-cell trait die before reaching maturity. Occurrence of the gene in high frequency in any given population accordingly implies some counterbalancing advantage in the heterozygotes. Heterozygous children have been shown to suffer potentially lethal attacks of *falciparum* malaria much less frequently than those lacking the gene entirely.

In most parts of Africa the sickle-cell gene occurs with a stable frequency (up to 40 per cent), matching the local intensity of *falciparum* malaria. In certain West African populations, however, no such balanced polymorphism has been attained. These include the primitive peoples to whom we have referred in connection with *ovale* malaria. It has been suggested that the sickle-cell gene was brought into this part of Africa by invaders from the east and has not yet had time to become established.[6]

Two hypotheses have been put forward regarding the origin of endemic *falciparum* malaria. Both associate it with the early development of settled agriculture which must certainly have been, on any theory, a crucial phase in the evolution of human disease. The first hypothesis involves the adaptation of *P. reichenowi* to man following on the introduction of iron-working into East Africa, about 2,000 years ago. This was followed by the extensive clearing of forests which may have led to increased contact between chimpanzees and man.

The second hypothesis involves a much earlier origin, possibly in Asia. It is based on the association between sickle-cell anaemia (and thalassaemia) and a condition, known as porotic hyperostosis, involving an enlargement of the marrow spaces in the bones, particularly of the skull. This condition occurs with high frequency in skulls from early Neolithic farming communities in marshy, but not in drier, areas of Greece, Anatolia and Cyprus. The varying frequencies of porotic hyperostosis in later skulls from the classical, Hellenistic and mediaeval periods in the Mediterranean area agrees well with what can be deduced from other sources regarding the intensity of malaria during those periods. The frequency in earlier finds is, however, extraordinarily high and this, coupled with the occurrence of a similar form of hyperostosis in early skulls from North America, has prompted the suggestion that some other form of anaemia may have been involved.

Ecology of Brugian Filariasis

The distribution of *Brugia* species as between various mammalian hosts is shown in Table 6.

The marked association with carnivores will be noted as will the much wider distribution among the primates than in the case of *Plasmodium*, both tree shrews and lorisids being infected. The subperiodic, swamp forest form of *B. malayi* is essentially a parasite of monkeys acquired by man as a zoonosis in areas where the swamp forest fringes on rice-cultivation. The nocturnally periodic form, associated with open swamps and rice-fields (Fig. 4, p. 25) is more highly adapted to man and may be exclusively dependent on him in parts of its range. The subperiodic form is adapted to vectors (*Mansonia* spp.) biting by day, as well as by night, in the shade of the forest. The periodic form is transmitted by night-biting species of *Mansonia* and *Anopheles*. The subperiodic form seems clearly to be the more primitive. It is thought to have evolved from ancestors resembling *B. pahangi*, which is primarily a parasite of swamp forest carnivores with primates as incidental hosts.

TABLE 6

Vertebrate hosts of *Brugia* species

Parasite	Carnivores	Hosts Primates	Other hosts
B. malayi	Domestic cat, Civet cat.	Man, Macaque, Leaf monkeys.	Pangolin.
B. pahangi	Domestic cat and dog, Tiger, Wild cats, Civet cats, Fishing cat.	Leaf monkey, Slow loris.	Pangolin, Moon rat, Giant squirrel.
B. patei	Domestic cat and dog, Genet.	Galago.	
B. ceylonensis	Domestic dog.	—	—
B. beaveri	Raccoon, ? Lynx.	—	—
B. guyanensis	Coatimundi, Grison.	—	—
B. tupaiae	—	Tree shrew	—
B. buckleyi	—	—	Ceylon hare.
B. sp. (Rhodesia)	Civet cat.	—	—
B. sp. (Timor)	—	Man.	—

The geographical distribution of the two forms of *B. malayi* is imperfectly known but it seems that the periodic form occupies most of the range (Fig. 13).

Although *Brugia* species are known for certain, in the New World, only from procyonid hosts (raccoon, coatimundi), microfilariae possibly belonging to this genus have been recovered from a lynx in Florida. Lynxes extend as far north as Alaska, the Canadian form being, apparently, conspecific with the European one. Entry into the New World, from an original homeland in South-east Asia, might therefore have taken place, in a host of this type, in the fairly recent past.

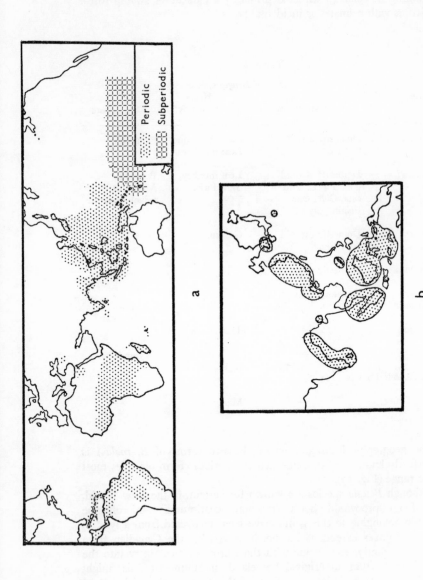

Fig. 13 Distribution of human filarial nematodes: **a** *Wuchereria bancrofti*, **b** *Brugia malayi*. The respective distributions of periodic and subperiodic *B. malayi* are imperfectly known. The former seems to occupy most of their joint range

Ecology of Wuchereria Bancrofti

The origins of the genus *Wuchereria* are obscure. The only recognized species is apparently confined to man and has never been successfully transferred to any other animal. The occurrence of isolated pockets of *W. bancrofti* in remote parts of Malaya, and of a rural Malayan strain poorly adapted to transmission by the urban vector, *Culex pipiens fatigans,* might be thought to betoken a South-east Asian origin. On the other hand *Wuchereria*-like microfilariae have recently been recovered from the African potto. There appears to be no reason to postulate the subperiodic Pacific form as primitive and the New World forms were almost certainly introduced in post-Columbian times. The principal rural vectors are *Anopheles* species in Africa and Asia and members of the *Aedes (Stegomyia) scutellaris* complex in Polynesia but various species of *Culex, Mansonia* and *Aedes* subgenera *Ochlerotatus* and *Finlaya* have been shown to be locally important in different parts of the range.

Urban Filariasis

A particularly serious problem is presented by the massive increases in *Culex fatigans* which have occurred in various urban centres in the tropics since the Second World War. As an example, a mosquito survey of Kaduna, in northern Nigeria, in 1942, failed to reveal any *fatigans*. In 1960 they were recorded in densities up to 760 per room per night. This increase seems to have taken place without comment from either the general public or the health service. There is evidence for large increases in other West African cities and in parts of East Africa and southern Asia.

The chief cause of such increases is to be found in the growth of cities and their suburbs and a failure of sanitary measures to keep pace with this growth. *Culex fatigans* breeds, by preference, in polluted water. Any increase in domestic or industrial waste is therefore liable to lead to its multiplication. A contributory factor may be the replacement of conventional methods of urban mosquito control by the use of DDT, dieldrin and other organic insecticides which *fatigans* tolerates better than most mosquitoes and to which it rapidly becomes resistant.

Filariasis is a disease of insidious onset and does not normally produce dramatic symptoms during the early years of an infection. Epidemiological assessment is accordingly difficult and the consequences of these increases in the vector are hard to predict, but they can scarcely be other than serious.

Ecology of Arboviruses

Of all the many mosquito-borne viruses less than a dozen have been studied, ecologically, in any detail. The problems are formidable. To identify the vectors it is not sufficient simply to find infected mosquitoes. Not all species which acquire the virus are necessarily capable of transmitting it. Even if they are potential transmitters their contact with susceptible hosts may be insufficient for them to transmit with any regularity. A variety of vertebrate hosts may be found infected or with antibodies but not all of these will circulate virus in sufficient quantity to infect the vectors. During inclement seasons virus may die down and become difficult or impossible to locate. There may be annual reintroduction by migratory hosts. Finally, ecological conditions may vary so that what is true at one time or place may not be true at another. How, in the face of this, different arboviruses maintain their ecological specificity is a challenging question.

Virus Encephalitides

Mosquito-borne viruses capable of causing severe encephalitis in man include Western and Eastern equine, in Group A, St Louis, Japanese B and Murray Valley, in Group B, and California encephalitis virus in the California Group.[8]

The last named differs from the others in being, it would seem, primarily a rodent virus, transmitted by species of *Aedes*. The first recorded human outbreak occurred as recently as 1964, in Indiana and neighbouring states, although the virus was discovered some fifteen years ago. The other viruses mentioned are essentially bird viruses associated either with marsh birds such as herons or with passerine birds feeding and nesting in marshy areas. Western equine encephalitis occurs mainly in the western United States though it has caused both human and equine outbreaks as far south as Argentina and as far north as southern Canada. The principal vector, *Culex tarsalis,* has a distribution approximately coterminous with that of the virus in North America. It feeds chiefly on birds but also, readily, on mammals, including man, and on reptiles. The mode of overwintering of the virus is still not fully understood. It has not been possible to find infected *C. tarsalis* between mid-November and mid-January even in southern California. Most *C. tarsalis* seem to feed on sugar, rather than blood, immediately prior to hibernation and it is thought that maintenance of virus may depend on small numbers of long-lived mosquitoes which engorged earlier. There is evidence for a build-up, or 'amplification', of virus in house sparrows before it appears in man and domestic fowls during epidemics.

Among the other encephalitis viruses the best studied is Japanese B. The principal vector of this virus, in Japan, is *Culex tritaeniorhynchus*. The primary hosts are herons and ibises, in which there is an extensive build-up of virus in the spring. Domestic pigs become infected during the summer and human infections follow somewhat later. Horses become infected concurrently with, but much less often than, the pigs. In South-east Asia the situation is somewhat different. There all-year-round transmission is possible and pigs are thought to provide a permanent reservoir of virus.

Yellow Fever

Yellow fever differs ecologically in many respects from the encephalitis viruses. Its principal, possibly its only, hosts are primates. *Culex* species play no part, so far as is known, in its transmission. It is enzootic only within the tropics. Viraemia, in primates, is short lived and immunity, probably, lifelong. The relatively slow reproductive turnover in these hosts implies that the reservoir must be a highly dynamic one, with the virus continually shifting from one focus to another within its main area of distribution, which comprises the humid forested areas of West and Central Africa and northern South America (Fig. 14).

For some time doubts have been felt as to the adequacy of such reservoirs for the survival of the virus. It has been suspected that some other more stable, probably more primitive, system exists though attempts to elucidate such a system have so far failed. In the drier parts of Africa antibodies to yellow fever virus have been recovered from galagos as far east as the Kenya coast and the islands of Zanzibar and Pemba. Curious, and at present unexplained, relationships exist between immunity rates in different types of host. Thus in northern Uganda and much of Kenya the infection appears to be largely con-

E

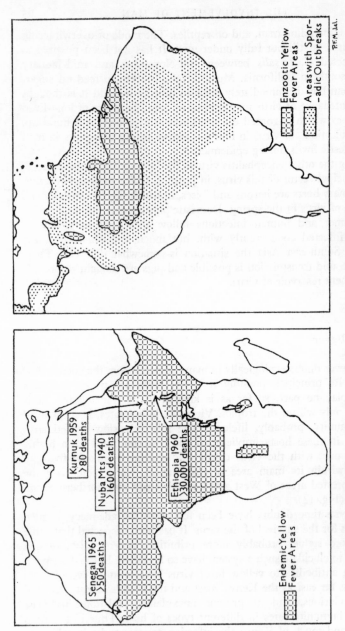

Fig. 14 Yellow fever in the Old and New World. By a system of rigorous quarantine the disease is currently confined to the areas shown. In South and Central America a campaign directed at the eradication of the urban vector, *Aedes aegypti*, has served to confine it to sporadic small-scale outbreaks in rural areas. In Africa massive outbreaks are still liable to occur. (Based on Strode, ref. 5, p. 28, and Soper, *Amer. J. publ. Hlth*, **53**:7, 1963.)

Enzootic Yellow Fever Areas

Areas with Spor–adic Outbreaks

Senegal 1965 >50 deaths

Nuba Mts 1940 >1600 deaths

Kurnuk 1959 >80 deaths

Ethiopia 1960 >30,000 deaths

Endemic Yellow Fever Areas

P.F.M. Lul.

fined to galagos but in the southern Sudan antibodies are rare in galagos, common in man and monkeys. In Zambia, northern Lesoto and Malawi there is a high incidence of antibodies in man and galagos, no evidence of infection in monkeys. Although some aspects of the epidemiology of yellow fever seem to be fairly well understood (see p. 78) it is evident that there are still large gaps in our knowledge of the natural history of this most lethal of all arbovirus diseases. Closely related viruses are known only from Africa and this, coupled with the generally greater tolerance on the part of African primates, seems strongly to suggest a post-Columbian introduction of yellow fever into South America by man.

Dengue

As we already noted (p. 52), the dengue syndrome can be produced by any one of several viruses. These include Chikungunya and Onyongnyong in Group A and West Nile and the true dengue viruses, types 1, 2, 3 and 4, in Group B. West Nile, which has been recorded from Israel, Egypt, East and South Africa and India, appears to resemble the encephalitis viruses in being primarily a virus of birds transmitted chiefly by *Culex*. The occurrence of true dengue viruses in non-human hosts has yet to be conclusively proved though antibodies to these, or to a very close relative, have been found in monkeys and other forest animals in Malaya. The disease was first recorded in epidemic form in India and Java in the late eighteenth century. During the present century there have been outbreaks in areas as widely separated as Greece, northern Queensland and Hawaii, though such outbreaks were relatively infrequent in South-east Asia until the recent appearance there of a new and lethal haemorrhagic form of the disease.

Haemorrhagic dengue was first recorded, unequivocally, in Manila in 1954 and in Bangkok in the same year, though there is some evidence for a small outbreak in Thailand as long ago as 1935. More recently outbreaks have been recorded from Singapore, Malaya, Laos, Vietnam and India. The disease appears to be becoming endemic over much of southern Asia. Unlike classical dengue, which is a painful and temporarily disabling, but not a lethal, disease, the haemorrhagic form is quite highly lethal especially to children.

Chikungunya virus was first isolated in East Africa in 1952. It was subsequently recovered during the haemorrhagic dengue epidemic in Bangkok in 1958 and has more recently caused massive epidemics in a number of cities in India. It does not, however, appear to produce haemorrhagic symptoms of a severe kind. The latter, so far as is known, are associated strictly with the classical dengue viruses.

Onyongnyong virus is closely related to Chikungunya and to the wild African Semliki Forest virus. It was first isolated from human cases in north-west Uganda in 1959. It subsequently spread southwards as far as Malawi, causing more than a million human cases. It is remarkable in being the only known human virus with anopheline mosquitoes as major vectors. The only vectors so far incriminated are *Anopheles gambiae* and *funestus*. Though still sub-lethal, Onyongnyong virus produces more severe symptoms than does Chikungunya. Semliki Forest is less pathogenic than either. Though shown to be transmissible by anophelines it has not been recovered from them in nature.

The involvement of man with all these viruses is clearly seen as the accompaniment to his progressive exploitation of his environment. Jungle yellow fever, in South America, is basically a disease of woodcutters, associated with the felling of trees and the bringing of infected canopy mosquitoes to the forest floor in clearings. Rural yellow fever, in East Africa, is associated with the cultivation of broad-leaved food plants which serve as breeding places for the rural vector, *Aedes simpsoni*. Western equine encephalitis is associated with irrigated farmland, Japanese B with rice-cultivation and pig-breeding. With increasing urbanization have come ecologically new diseases, urban dengue, urban yellow fever, haemorrhagic dengue, urban filariasis. Finally, in the very recent past, man has developed a new mode of exploitation, the large scale employment of synthetic insecticides. It is hard to believe that the emergence of Onyongnyong fever, the first anopheline-borne virus disease of man, has followed so closely, only by coincidence, on the use of these insecticides to alter the balance between anthropophilic and zoophilic *Anopheles*.

REFERENCES

1. BAER, J. G. (Ed.). 1957, *First Symposium on Host Specificity among Parasites of Vertebrates*. Neuchatel: Institut de Zoologie
2   CLARK, W. Le Gros, 1965, *History of the Primates*. 9th Edn., London: British Museum (Natural History).
3. BOYD, M. F. (Ed.), 1949, *Malariology*. Philadelphia: Saunders.

4. COLE, S., 1965, *Races of Man*. 2nd Edn. London: British Museum (Natural History).
5. BRUCE-CHWATT, L. J., 1965, 'Palaeogenesis and palaeo-epidemiology of primate malaria'. *Bull. Wld Hlth Org.*, **32**: 363–387.
6. LIVINGSTONE, F. B., 1958, 'Anthropological implications of sickle-cell gene distribution in West Africa'. *Am. Anthrop.*, **60**: 533–562.
7. ANDREWES, C. H., 1967, *The Natural History of Viruses*. London: Weidenfeld & Nicholson.
8. REEVES, W. C., 1965, 'Ecology of mosquitoes in relation to arboviruses'. *A. Rev. Ent.*, **10**: 25–46.

V

The Mosquitoes: a General Conspectus

MOSQUITOES are two-winged flies (Diptera) belonging to the suborder Nematocera and the family Culicidae. Some authors also include in this family the dixid and chaoborid midges, which are certainly closely related. We, however, prefer to place these in separate families and to restrict the Culicidae entirely to the mosquitoes. In this, as in almost all other respects, we shall follow the current world catalogue.[1] The present chapter will be devoted to a brief survey of the Culicidae, following the outline classification shown in Table 7. We shall try to mention all the important vectors in each group, bearing in mind that information on this point is still by no means complete.

Sources of error in the past have included a failure to recognize the source of infections in the vector, and thus to mistake non-human parasites for those infective to man, and the placing of too much emphasis on the mere numbers of the vector as opposed to its true epidemiological potential in terms of longevity. On the other side of the picture there has been a tendency to minimize unduly the importance of comparatively wild vectors. Rural disease, affecting small, scattered populations, can be cumulatively just as important as the more dramatic outbreaks in densely populated areas. Nor, of course, can any situation, however trivial or remote, be safely ignored where eradication, rather than merely control, is the objective.

Subfamily Anophelinae

Gross characters distinguishing this family include a characteristic resting attitude, and general facies, of the adult, floating eggs, laid singly, and the possession of larvae highly specialized for life at the surface film. Larval adaptations include the loss, or non-development, of a respiratory siphon, the presence of 'float hairs' on all or most abdominal segments and the ability to rotate the head through 180°

while feeding. Three genera are included, two of them, the neotropical *Chagasia* and Australiasian *Bironella*, very small and of no known medical importance and the third, *Anopheles*, very large with about 350 species. No recent comprehensive account of the genus is available. For regional monographs the reader should consult a bibliographic survey.[2] Two important recent monographs are listed in the bibliography on p. 82.

TABLE 7

Classification of mosquitoes

Subfamily	Anophelinae		
Genus	*Anopheles*		
	Bironella		
	Chagasia		
Subfamily	Toxorhynchitinae		
Genus	*Toxorhynchites*		
Subfamily	Culicinae		
Tribe	Sabethini	Tribe	Culicini
Genus	*Sabethes*	Genus	*Culex*
	Wyeomyia		*Uranotaenia*
	Phoniomyia		*Hodgesia*
	Limatus		*Ficalbia*
	Trichoprosopon		*Mansonia*
	Tripteroides		*Aedeomyia*
	Malaya		*Zeugnomyia*
	Topomyia		*Orthopodomyia*
			Psorophora
			Udaya
			Eretmapodites
			Armigeres
			Heizmannia
			Haemagogus
			Aedes
			Opifex
			Culiseta
			Deinocerites

Genus Anopheles

This includes all the known vectors of human and simian malaria as well as the major vectors of rural bancroftian filariasis within its area of distribution. (The absence of anopheline mosquitoes from Polynesia and Micronesia was noted previously, p. 59.) It is all the more remarkable that, although some dozen different arboviruses have been isolated from wild-caught *Anopheles*, Onyongnyong is the only one of which it is known to be an important vector to man (p. 68). Six subgenera are recognized. We shall mention only those which include known vectors of human disease.

Subgenus Kerteszia

All six species of this subgenus are neotropical. One of them breeds in bamboo internodes. The others breed in the leaf-axils of epiphytic bromeliads (see Pl. II). Feeding takes place mainly in the forest canopy and in the forest fringes of which the canopy is ecologically an extension. (The bromeliads themselves are invaders of the forest, stemming from saxicolous ancestors with which they share the ability to grow in minimal quantities of soil.) Some of the species will readily leave the forest and invade human settlements to feed. One of them, *An. cruzii*, from Brazil, is suspected as a potential vector of simian malaria (p. 42). Another, *An. bellator*, was formerly responsible for severe outbreaks of 'bromeliad malaria' in Trinidad (Ref. 3, p. 68). This resulted from the invasion, by bromeliads, of immortelle trees planted as shade trees in the cocoa plantations. Control could eventually be effected by spraying the bromeliads with copper sulphate solution on a massive scale (Pl. II).

Subgenus Anopheles

This comprises some 120 species. They are divided into six series, two of which, Series *Myzorhynchus* and Series *Anopheles*, contain important disease vectors. The first is mainly, though not exclusively, tropical in distribution, the second mainly temperate and subtropical with some species groups occurring mainly or partly within

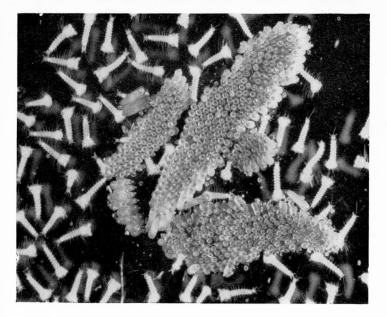

ATE I

Egg raft and newly hatched larvae of *Culex fatigans*. With the advent of residual insect-
des attention shifted from the breeding place to the dwelling house as an accessible focus
the mosquito population. But breeding places are also oviposition sites and, as such,
ective foci of potential vectors since each of these must oviposit several times between
coming infected and becoming infective.

*otograph by Joe O'Neal and J. S. Haeger, Florida State Board of Health Entomological Research
nter, Vero Beach.*

. Tree shrew (*Tupaia* sp). Growing interest in primatology and the continual discovery of
ew mosquito-borne zoonoses have combined to focus attention on these, supposedly the
most primitive primates. Up to the present they have failed to yield any malaria parasites or
rboviruses but they are subject to an interesting form of Brugian filariasis.

Photo: Ministry of Health, Trinidad.

PLATE II Bromeliad malaria in Trinidad

a. Epiphytic bromeliads in situ. Also shown is a bromeliad picker. Attempts at clearing the bromeliads by hand were unsuccessful. Owing to

b. Eventually malaria, transmitted by anophelines utilizing the bromeliads for breeding places, was controlled by spraying them with

a

PLATE III

Desert Malaria. The photographs were taken at Sodom, in the salt desert at the southern end of the Dead Sea.

a. The vector, *Anopheles sergenti*, feeds on man, dogs and the cattle which are grazed on the salt-marsh vegetation.

b. During the daytime it takes refuge in caves resembling those in which the Dead Sea Scrolls were found, penetrating deep into crevices in the rock.

(Photos: Author)

b

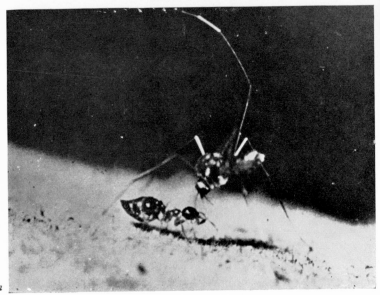

PLATE IV

b

Sabethine mosquitoes

a. *Malaya genurostris* soliciting re-
gurgitated food from an ant. In this
genus the proboscis is highly modified
and this is the only known method of
feeding.

(*Photo: W. W. Macdonald*)

b. *Sabethes chloropterus* ovipositing.
The abdomen is tucked forward and
the eggs are projected into very small
tree-holes of the kind shown (from
Galindo, *Am. J. trop. Med. Hyg.*, 7:
431, 1958).

the tropics. Series *Myzorhynchus* includes important South-east Asian malaria and filariasis vectors belonging to the *An. barbirostris, hyrcanus* and *umbrosus* complexes. Other members of this series appear to feed mainly on wild and domestic ungulates. *An. barbirostris* is a vector of Chittoor virus of cattle (a member of the Bunyamwera Group) in India. Some members of the *An. umbrosus* complex are known or suspected vectors of *Plasmodium traguli* of mouse deer.

Series *Anopheles* includes a number of very distinct species groups. The *An. maculipennis* complex, which will be dealt with in more detail later, includes a number of species formerly of great importance as malaria vectors in temperate and subtropical latitudes in both hemispheres. Most of these have been rendered harmless by the advance of eradication but the related *An. pseudopunctipennis* still presents some difficult problems in Mexico as does *An. sacharovi* in the eastern Mediterranean. Most *Anopheles* breed in various kinds of ground water but two species groups in the present series, one southern Asian, the other holarctic, breed in tree-holes. One member of the holarctic group, *An. plumbeus*, is thought to have been responsible for two recent cases of indigenous malaria in London. Only one species of Series *Anopheles* is known from Africa. This is the very interesting *An. concolor* of gallery forests in the former Belgian Congo, a suspected vector of *Plasmodium cephalophi* of antelopes.

Subgenus Cellia

This includes about 160 species. The six series into which it is divided all include important malaria vectors. The African forest-dwelling members of Series *Neomyzomyia* are thought to be the most primitive members of the series. They include *An. dureni*, the vector of *Plasmodium berghei* and its allies, of forest rats (p. 44), also other species, frequenting rock shelters and burrows and transmitting *P. atheruri* of porcupines and still others which are wholly or partly cavernicolous and transmit bat malaria. None of the African species are major vectors of human malaria though one, *An. nili*, may possibly be locally important. Although most of the African species are markedly shade-loving, one species group (*An. rhodesiensis* and its allies) has penetrated far into the arid zones and is found in such inhospitable areas as the Sinai Peninsula and the Hadhramaut.

The oriental *Neomyzomyia* are also mainly forest mosquitoes with one species, *An. kochi*, adapted to more open habitats where it feeds on ungulates. The *An. leucosphyrus* complex includes important vectors of human malaria (*An. leucosphyrus* in southern Borneo, *An. balabacensis* elsewhere). Other members of the complex are vectors of simian malaria. *An. balabacensis* feeds on both man and monkeys and is considered a potential vector of simian malaria to man. Still further east, in Melanesia and northern Australia, where *Neomyzomyia* is the dominant group of *Cellia*, the association with forest largely breaks down. Members of the *An. punctulatus* complex are the major vectors of human malaria in that part of the world.

Series *Myzomyia* is the dominant group of anophelines in Africa where it includes the very important malaria vector, *An. funestus*. Related species which are important malaria vectors in southern Asia include *An. minimus, culicifacies* and *fluviatilis*. Although many of them prefer shaded breeding places the members of this series are essentially savanna and woodland species in contrast to *Neomyzomyia*. *An. sergenti* is an important vector in arid parts of the Near East (see Pl. III). Besides being important vector of bancroftian filariasis, *An. funestus* is the principal vector of Onyongnyong fever (p. 68).

Series *Pyretophorus* includes the various members of the *An. gambiae* complex, among them important vectors of malaria, filariasis and Onyongnyong. This complex will be discussed in detail later. The related *An. sundaicus* is a very important brackish-water-breeding malaria vector in southern Asia. All the members of this series occur as brackish water forms, even the east African highland *An. christyi*, which is sometimes found breeding in volcanic pools with high mineral content. Desert species commonly possess a similar ability associated with the concentration of mineral salts in their breeding places by evaporation. An example is *An. multicolor*, a member of Series *Paramyzomyia*. This species and its allies are distinguished by the complete or almost complete suppression of the egg-floats (p. 83).

Series *Neocellia* includes three major vectors of malaria. *An. superpictus* is a Mediterranean species extending into north-west India. Though less important than formerly, owing to its sensitivity to insecticides, it still presents problems in certain areas owing to its exophilic habits (p. 128). *An. maculatus* is a species of spring-fed streams in South-east Asia. It is locally important as a vector in Malaya but not, apparently, elsewhere. *An. stephensi* is a major vector in Iraq and Persia, along the Arabian shore of the Persian Gulf and in parts of India. Its ability to breed in wells and cisterns renders it an important urban, as well as a rural, vector. It has become doubly resistant to insecticides of both the DDT and the dieldrin group and is probably now the most formidable of all malaria vectors, second only to *An. gambiae*. Interestingly, it has recently been found on the Red Sea coast of Egypt, apparently as a relict, rather than an introduced, population. It has a close relative, *An. dancalicus,* in Ethiopia.

Series *Cellia* comprises three African species, one of which, *An. pharoensis,* is an important malaria vector in lower Egypt. Like *An. multicolor* and other desert species it is said to have an exceptionally long flight range. It was recently found, for the first time for many years, along the Mediterranean coast of Israel, where it was associated with an outbreak of malaria and proved to be dieldrin-resistant, suggesting a possible wind-borne introduction from the Nile delta.

Subgenus Nyssorhynchus

This is the New World counterpart of subgenus *Cellia*. It extends from Argentina to the extreme south of the United States. It includes, as important malaria vectors in Central America, the Caribbean area and northern South America, *An. albimanus, aquasalis* and *darlingi.* Some other species, e.g. *An. nunez-tovari,* may be important locally. *An. aquasalis* and *darlingi* are vectors of wuchererian filariasis.

Subfamily Toxorhynchitinae

This contains a single genus, *Toxorhynchites* (formerly called *Megarhinus*), with about fifty species. Most of them are very large with wing length up to a centimetre. As with some of the larger species of culicine, the larvae are obligatory predators on those of other species. They have the mouthbrush hairs modified to form stout, curved setae (Fig. 15).

The prey is seized with the stout, toothed mandibles and devoured with the aid of the modified mouthbrushes. Various small aquatic animals serve as prey but the principal food consists of the larvae of other mosquitoes. Some degree of cannibalism on larvae of their own species occurs in the absence of alternative food. The breeding places are container habitats of various kinds (see p. 95).

The adults of both sexes are highly modified for nectar-feeding. The proboscis is long and recurved through an obtuse angle, rendering blood-feeding quite impossible. The abdomen is modified for hovering flight in a manner reminiscent of, for example, bee-hawk moths. Many

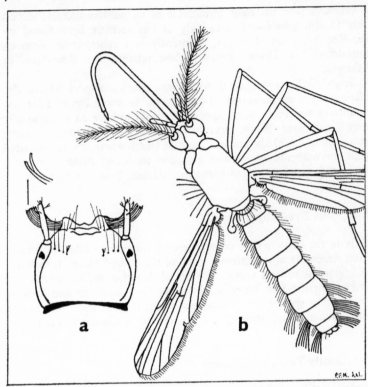

Fig. 15 *Toxorhynchites*. **a** Head of larva showing mouthbrushes modified for predation. **b** Adult female with long, curved proboscis, employed in nectar-feeding and flattened abdomen with lateral scale tufts associated with hovering flight.

species have brilliant metallic colours. Several have been introduced into Pacific islands with a view to controlling container-breeding *Stegomyia* which transmit filariasis. Their value for this purpose is, however, slight since their rate of reproduction is slow and the numbers of larvae in individual breeding places are always small. The genus is found throughout the Old and New World tropics with excursions into the eastern United States, the maritime provinces of the USSR and Japan. No species occur in Polynesia other than those introduced by man.

Subfamily Culicinae

This is the largest of the culicid subfamilies. It includes two tribes, the Culicini and Sabethini. The latter are distinguished by various distinctive characters, almost all of which are, however, shared with individual culicine genera. A distinctive feature is the suppression of the ventral brush of the larva, possibly associated with breeding in leaf-axils though this habit has now been lost by many species (see below). The adults adopt a characteristic attitude, both in flight and at rest, with the hind tarsi carried forward over the head (see Pl. IV).

Tribe Sabethini

This group has undergone an extensive radiation in the New World tropics and in eastern Asia and Melanesia. A few species occur outside the tropics in both hemispheres, notably *Wyeomyia smithii* which is found as far north as Newfoundland and westwards across southern Canada to the western end of the Great Lakes. This species breeds in plant pitchers (*Sarracenia purpurea*). The larvae regularly survive the winter though frozen solid. It does not appear to differ conspicuously, in other respects, from its neotropical relatives. Many species breed in leaf-axil habitats, including axils of epiphytic bromeliads, pitcher plants and flower bracts and spathes. Others, such as the majority of species of the large Old World genus *Tripteroides*, breed in tree-holes, sometimes very small ones (Pl. IV) or in bamboos. Larvae of the axil-breeding Old World genera *Malaya and Topomyia* have the maxillae armed with stout spines as do the larvae of some New World species. These larvae are probably either predatory or necrophagous. A similar condition is found in an extreme form in pitcher plant larvae of *Tripteroides* subgenus *Rachisoura* (p. 98 and Fig. 22, p. 97). None of the sabethines are known to transmit any disease to man but *Sabethes chloropterus* is thought to have played a part in the massive yellow fever epizootic which swept through Central America during the 1950s.

Tribe Culicini

This is a large and diverse group, not readily classified ecologically since some genera show considerable plasticity. For general purposes, however, the following groups may be recognized:

1. Aedine genera, characterized by the possession of drought-resistant eggs permitting the utilization of ground-pool and container habitats in both of which the eggs are laid above the water-line. Included in this group are the very large genus *Aedes,* with some 750 species, occupying both types of habitat and the related ground-pool- and rock-pool-breeding genera *Psorophora and Opifex.*

2. Quasi-sabethine genera exhibiting both aedine and sabethine features. These include *Heizmannia, Haemagogus, Zeugnomyia, Eretmapodites, Udaya* and *Armigeres.* They are all container-breeders utilizing, particularly, bamboos and tree-holes (leaf-axils or fallen leaves in *Zeugnomyia* and a few species of *Eretmapodites*).

3. Genera associated with dense acquatic vegetation: *Ficalbia, Hodgesia, Uranotaenia, Mansonia, Aedeomyia.*

4. Miscellaneous genera: *Culex, Deinocerites, Culiseta, Orthopodomyia.* No attempt will be made, at this point, to discuss the biology of these genera in detail. We shall return to them, as and when appropriate, later. All that will be attempted here is a summary of their medical significance, if any, and the salient features of their ecology.

Among container-breeders belonging to subgenus *Stegomyia* of *Aedes* are the principal vectors of yellow fever in Africa. These are the tree-hole-breeding *Ae. africanus,* which feeds in the canopy and is considered to be the principal vector from monkey to monkey, *Ae. simpsoni,* breeding in axils of broad-leafed plants, such as yam, banana and pineapple, and a major vector to man in rural epidemics, and the cosmopolitan urban vector *Ae. aegypti.* The latter is also the major vector of both classical and haemorrhagic dengue. Other dengue vectors, whose epidemiological potential still requires to be adequately investigated, include *Ae.* (*St.*) *albopictus* in South-east Asia and members of the *Ae. scutellaris* complex in the Pacific area. The role of members of this complex as vectors of bancroftian filariasis has already been mentioned (p. 48). *Ae.* (*Ochlerotatus*) *vigilax* has been incriminated as a vector of filariasis in New Caledonia. This is a somewhat aberrant member of the subgenus *Ochlerotatus* which occurs, characteristically in higher latitudes in both hemispheres, extending into the high Arctic (but not the Antarctic). Virus-carriers breeding in flooded grassland or woodland pools include *Ae.* (*Ochl.*) *caballus* on the high veldt and *Ae.* (*Neomelaniconion*) *circumluteolus* on the low veldt of South Africa. Some species of *Ochlerotatus* may be involved in the transmission of North American encephalitis viruses and *Ae.*

(*Aedimorphus*) *vexans*, and perhaps some other species, are concerned in the transmission of Tahyna virus in central Europe. Several viruses, particularly Ilheus, have been recovered from *Psorophora ferox* but the vector status of this and other members of the genus requires further assessment. *Opifex* is a highly curious monotypic genus breeding in seashore pools in New Zealand. It bites man readily but is not known to transmit any disease. We shall have more to say about its biology later.

The quasi-sabethine group also includes important arbovirus vectors, particularly in the genus *Haemagogus*. This includes canopy-feeding species which are probably the major maintenance vectors of jungle yellow fever in South America. A part in this is also played by *Ae.* (*Finlaya*) species, notably *Ae. leucocelaenus*. *Heizmannia* is the Oriental counterpart of *Haemagogus*, which it resembles sufficiently to give rise to the suspicion that it may well prove to be involved in the transmission of forest viruses in South-east Asia when these are more fully investigated. Both yellow fever virus and rift valley virus have been recovered from *Eretmapodites* species and *E. chrysogaster* has been shown to transmit yellow fever by bite in the laboratory.

Among the genera associated with aquatic vegetation, *Uranotaenia* is a very large group one section of which occurs in container habitats. One subgenus of *Ficalbia* also occupies such habitats while retaining some features adaptive to swamp breeding. The most highly adapted genera in this group are *Aedeomyia* and *Mansonia* (Fig. 16).

Mansonia (formerly called *Taeniorhynchus*) is a medically very important genus. Its biology has been intensively studied, particularly in relation to brugian filariasis.[5] One species, *M. uniformis*, has been shown to transmit wuchererian filariasis in New Guinea. Viruses have occasionally been isolated from other species. The larvae have a highly modified siphon enabling them to obtain oxygen from the submerged roots of aquatic plants and, in some cases, specialized waterside trees. The genus as a whole has a very wide distribution in the Old and New World tropics extending eastwards into Melanesia, northwards into North America, western Eurasia and Japan and southwards to New Zealand. Some authors recognize two genera, *Mansonia* and *Coquillettidia*, but it is not clear that this serves any useful purpose.

Aedeomyia larvae are quite differently adapted to the same general habitat. They have flattened antennae, stellate hairs on the thorax and abdomen, and greatly elongated lateral and shoulder hairs permitting close apposition either to the surface film or to the air film trapped on the under side of floating leaves. The integument is weakly sclerotized

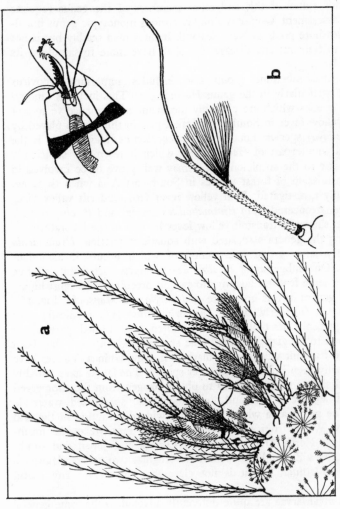

Fig. 16 Larvae of genera associated with aquatic vegetation. **a** *Aedeomyia* showing the great development of fringed setae associated with close application to the under side of floating leaves, etc. Other specialized features of this genus are discussed in the text. **b** *Mansonia* showing the siphon modified for piercing sub-aqueous plant tissues and the antenna with greatly elongated distal portion.

and the tracheal system markedly reduced. Respiration is thought to take place through the entire body surface and the larvae can survive exceptionally long periods at the bottom of the breeding places. None of the genera in this group, other than *Mansonia*, are known to be associated with the transmission of disease.

In the miscellaneous group of genera *Orthopodomyia* is a widespread group of specialized tree-hole-breeding species, with interesting features recalling *Anopheles*, two of which bite man occasionally. Others are suspected as potential vectors of eastern and western equine encephalitis among birds. *Deinocerites* (see Pl. V) is a small genus, apparently related to *Culex*, very highly specialized for crab-hole breeding and with some noteworthy behavioural peculiarities which will be discussed later. St Louis encephalitis virus has been isolated from one species in Panama. *Culiseta*, formerly called *Theobaldia*, is a genus of some forty species with an almost world-wide distribution outside the tropics and with two tropical species in Africa. *C. melanura* is an important maintenance vector of Eastern equine encephalitis in uninhabited swamps in the United States, but although several other species of this genus bite man none is known to transmit disease to him. The bulk of species breed in ground pools, but one African species is found in tree-holes, several others in different parts of the range invade domestic containers and a number of Australasian species breed in crab-holes.

The genus *Culex* is a very large one with some 600 species. It appears to be basically a ground-pool-breeding group though with species occurring in a variety of container habitats and with a few associated with dense aquatic vegetation. The eggs are laid in rafts, as in some sabethines and some *Culiseta*, and have only a limited tolerance of desiccation. Thus, although very widely distributed, it is excluded from the extreme northern latitudes conquered by *Aedes*. Among dark-legged species *Culex pipiens* ssp. *fatigans* is the major urban vector of periodic wucherearian filariasis. The large group of banded-legged species, also belonging to the typical subgenus, includes major vectors of western equine encephalitis (*C. tarsalis*), Japanese B encephalitis (*C. gelidus*, *C. tritaeniorhynchus*) and Murray Valley encephalitis (*C. annulirostris*). *C. p. fatigans* may also play a part in the transmission of Japanese B and St Louis encephalitis under urban epidemic conditions. *C. p. var. molestus* is a vector of West Nile virus in Egypt and may be a vector of wucherearian filariasis in the same country.

F

REFERENCES

1. STONE, A., KNIGHT, K. L. & STARCKE, H., 1959, *A Synoptic Catalog of the Mosquitoes of the World.* Washington, D.C.: Thomas Say Foundation.
2. SMART, J., 1956, *A Handbook for the Identification of Insects of Medical Importance.* 3rd Edn. London: British Museum (Natural History).
3. GILLIES, M. T. & DE MEILLON, B., 1968, *The Anophelinae of Africa South of the Sahara.* Johannesburg: South African Institute for Medical Research.
4. REID, J. A., 1968, *Anopheline Mosquitoes of Malaya and Borneo.* Kuala Lumpur: Institute for Medical Research.
5. WHARTON, R. H., 1962, *The Biology of Mansonia Mosquitoes in Relation to the Transmission of Filariasis in Malaya.* Kuala Lumpur: Institute for Medical Research.

VI

Mosquito Biology: the Early Stages

THE course of development from fertilized egg to adult is broadly the same in all mosquitoes. Oviposition is followed by maturation of the embryo, hatching, three successive larval moults, pupation and, finally, emergence of the adult. Within the limits imposed by a life-history of this kind, there is great variation in detail. Much of this is beyond the scope of this book and we shall be able to deal only with selected examples. Nevertheless, although they do not themselves transmit disease, the early stages of mosquitoes play a major role in determining the form which diseases assume. This is reflected in the very considerable attention paid to their biology[1, 2, 3]. Detailed studies of embryology and physiology are also outside our scope. For these the reader must refer to the specialist literature.

The Mosquito Egg

Most of those mosquito eggs so far described have the shape of an elongated ellipse with the anterior end broader than the posterior and the major axis at least twice as long as the minor. Exceptions are provided by *Toxorhynchites,* in which the egg is subspherical (Fig. 17a), *Mansonia,* subgenus *Mansonioides,* in which the anterior end is drawn out into a spine-like prolongation (Fig. 17b) and some species of *Sabethes* and *Wyeomyia* in which the egg is rhomboidal (Fig. 17c).

The delicate outer layer (exochorion) of the egg-shell is covered to a greater or less extent with small tubercles forming a characteristic pattern. The mechanical strength of the shell is provided by the tough endochorion which, in most cases, darkens after laying and in genera such as *Aedes* and *Psorophora* exhibits characteristic scultpturing (Fig. 17d). In the eggs of most *Anopheles* the exochorion is drawn out into a lateral frill which is usually expanded along all or most of its length to form a pair of floats (Fig. 17e and see Pl. V, p. 120). The

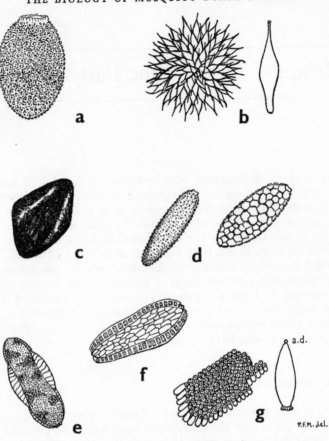

Fig. 17. Mosquito eggs and egg masses. **a** *Toxorhynchites*, **b** *Mansonia* subgenus *Mansonioides*, **c** *Sabethes*, **d** *Aedes*, **e** *Anopheles maculipennis* s.l., **f** *Orthopodomyia*, **g** *Culex* (a.d. Apical droplet).

floatless eggs of *Paramyzomyia* (p. 74) are said to float upright in the water. Eggs of this kind furnish valuable taxonomic characters provided due account is taken of individual and strain variation and of the seasonal variation which sometimes occurs. Such characters are of course genetically maternal since they are imposed on the egg by the mother. In the *Anopheles maculipennis* complex use is made of diag-

nostic differences in the pattern on the upper surface of the egg resulting from variations in the size and density of packing of the
exochorionic tubercles and the differing degrees to which the dark
endochorion is thereby obscured (Fig. 17e).

No known culicine eggs have floats, though the eggs of
Toxorhynchites are sufficiently buoyant to float with the crown above
water. *Orthopodomyia* eggs have a complex lateral flange recalling
the lateral frill of *Anopheles* but serving quite a different function
(Fig. 17f). In this genus the eggs are laid above the water-line on the
inner walls of tree-holes and the lateral flange is said to serve the
function of attachment. In these, as in other mosquito eggs, hatching
is by dehiscence of an apical cap aided by a small spine or 'egg-
burster' on the head of the first-stage larva.

In *Culex*, some *Culiseta*, some *Armigeres*, some *Uranotaenia*, some
Mansonia and some sabethines the eggs are compacted into masses.
These may take the form of irregular aggregations, ribbons or compact
rafts in which the eggs are kept upright with the hydrophobic anterior
end downwards (Fig. 17g). In the rafts of *Culex* and *Culiseta* species
the posterior pole of the egg carries a small droplet of fluid with
surfactant properties which may assist in the righting of capsized rafts
and also, it seems, serve to repel egg-scavengers. *Mansonia* subgenera
Mansonia and *Mansonioides* glue their eggs in small masses to the
under side of floating plants (Fig. 17b). In other subgenera they are
laid in floating rafts.

The strongly resistant eggs of *Aedes* and *Psorophora* can withstand
desiccation for months. In other cases the equivalent period is measurable in days or, granted a reasonably moist substrate, weeks. Eggs of
some sabethines and quasi-sabethines are said to sink almost
immediately after laying. Two species of *Anopheles* have been shown
to overwinter in the egg but this is very exceptional except in *Aedes*.
Recent detailed studies of the egg of *Culex pipiens*, aided by electron
scan microscopy (Pl. V, p. 120) have shown that the exochorion comprises two sheets, the outer forming an open network over most of
the surface. Between these is a thin layer of trapped air, or plastron,
causing the under surface of the egg to appear lighter should it float
on its side and the anterior end to appear lighter when in the normal
position. It may also serve to abet respiration should the eggs be submerged.

Depth of larval diapause, in species with resistant eggs, is under
genetic control and wide variation in response to hatching stimuli may
occur as between individuals. Species with only one generation in the
year may, nevertheless, show a succession of hatches during the

favourable season. Egg diapause in *Ae. triseriatus* is induced mainly by shorter photoperiod, with enhancement by lowered temperature as with adult hibernation in other species. In both cases there are interesting effects of latitude on the critical photoperiod. In lower latitudes *Ae. triseriatus* can hibernate either in the egg or in the larval stage, but reduced photoperiod fails to induce diapause in larvae from more northerly latitudes.

Simple immersion is not, in general, sufficient to induce hatching of aedine eggs. The other factors involved are complex but the additional stimulus seems normally to be provided mainly by a reduction in the available free oxygen. In the laboratory it is customary to employ reducing agents or, better, organic infusions. Hatching can also be induced by carbon monoxide and this effect has been shown to be photolabile and so, perhaps, to involve cytochrome oxidase inhibition. Using a very narrow light-beam with bleached eggs, the site of action of the hatching stimulus has been located at the anterior end of the larva. Acetylcholine assays have been taken to suggest that changes in the threshold of stimulation are associated with changes in the overall nervous activity of the larva.

Larval Biology

In the previous chapter we employed a very simplified classification of larval habitats. Here we shall introduce a rather more complicated one. Before doing so, however, a few points of a general nature need emphasis. Most species of mosquito can be categorized reasonably sharply with respect to their breeding places. Nevertheless a certain degree of plasticity has to be allowed for. Larvae of species normally breeding in leaf habitats will sometimes be found breeding in bamboos or tree-holes. Species breeding in tree-holes are often found in bamboos or rock-holes, less often in plant axils. The effect may be especially pronounced where adaptation to a particular type of highly specialized breeding place enables a species to gain a marked local ascendancy. As an example *Ae* (*Ochl.*) *natronius*, breeding in volcanic pools hot and alkaline enough to take the skin off a foot incautiously inserted into them, will be found swarming in ordinary freshwater ground pools in the immediate vicinity. *Eretmapodites* species breeding in the fermenting contents of split cocoa pods have been known to 'overspill' into peridomestic container habitats to the exclusion of species normally found in them. Introduced species faced with little or no competition in their preferred habitat may behave similarly.

There are, however, limits to the potentialities of even the most plastic species. Container breeders are rarely found in ground pools (other than rock pools). Ground-pool species rarely breed in containers, though there are some exceptions, especially among *Culex* species. It follows from this that, while it is perfectly possible to construct usable categories of larval habitats, these will be found, in many cases at least, to refer rather to preferences than to absolute requirements. They are, moreover, preferences on the part of the gravid female, rather than of the larvae, since it is she who 'chooses' the breeding place. With this proviso the following classification of larval habitats will be adopted:

A. Running-water habitats

B. Still-water habitats
1. Ground-water habitats
a. Permanent
b. Temporary
2. Subterranean habitats
a. Artificial
b. Natural
3. Container habitats
a. Tree-holes
b. Bamboos
c. Leaf habitats
d. Fruits and husks
e. Artificial containers
f. Miscellaneous

Running-water Habitats

These are generally a much more important source of anopheline mosquitoes than of culicines. Some medically important *Culex* species, such as *C. tritaeniorhynchus*, breed in slow-running ditches or irrigation channels where emergent or overhanging vegetation offers protection from the current. Highly polluted and partly blocked drains or ditches are an important source of *C. p. fatigans*. A few other species of this genus gain protection from the current in masses of filamentous green algae. *Aedes* species are nearly always conspicuous by their absence from running-water habitats.

With anophelines the situation is quite different. The edges of streams, irrigation and drainage channels and slowly-running rivers are a major breeding place of many species, always provided that some form of protection from the current is available to augment the drag exerted by the banks. In the absence of vegetation protection may be afforded by stony shallows. Species such as *An. superpictus,* occurring in such situations, may be most abundant in the dry season when the water is at its shallowest or even when it has disappeared from sight among gravel.

The practice of shading stream edges to control such species as *An. minimus, An. maculatus* or *An. albimanus* depends for its success less on any direct effect of the larvae than on destruction of the marginal vegetation required to provide them with an anchorage.[4] Larvae of *An. minimus* are positively attracted to shade and thrive best when provided with it. They show a combination of activation by exposure to light, positive attraction to shade and an avoidance reaction to strong light, once the shade is attained, which keeps them close to the bank. Here they can resist currents of up to 0.3 feet per second (equivalent to, perhaps, three feet per second in midstream). Species breeding in more exposed situations can resist flushing by lying on the bottom, sometimes for periods running into hours.

Still-water Habitats

Under this heading we have refrained from including swamps or marshes as a separate category, as is often done. In our view these are best treated as collections of smaller ground-water habitats rather than as habitats in themselves. The same applies to lakes and ponds, the edges of which often provide a whole range of habitats round a single perimeter. Rock pools might perhaps have been included as a separate category, intermediate in many respects between ground pools and container habitats and sometimes harbouring a specialized fauna of *Aedes* or *Uranotaenia* species. Even when exposed they may also serve as an alternative breeding place for tree-hole breeders such as *Stegomyia* or *Haemagogus* species. When heavily shaded and containing dead leaves they may support a typical tree-hole fauna. Earth-lined ground pools, on the other hand, are markedly unattractive to container-breeders other than some species of *Culex*.

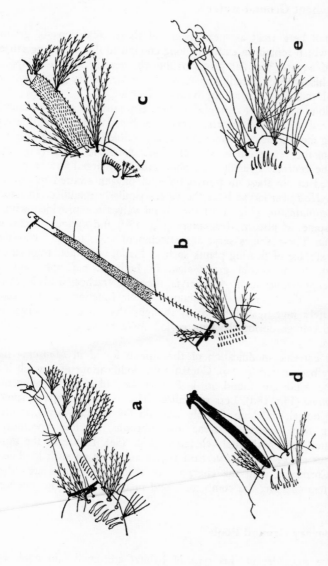

Fig. 18 Larval siphons. **a** *Culex poicilipes.* **b** *Culex argenteopunctatus.* **c** *Aedeomyia furfurea.* **d** *Ficalbia pallida* **e** *Ficalbia minima.* These are all species associated with dense aquatic vegetation. For explanation see text.

Permanent Ground-water

We shall here treat as 'permanent' all those collections of ground water which remain in existence long enough to develop a specialized flora of aquatic vascular plants. Although there is some overlapping both this type of breeding place and the temporary pool have, in general, their own specialized mosquito fauna.

Various species of *Anopheles* and *Uranotaenia* are particularly associated with dense aquatic vegetation, but without exhibiting any striking morphological adaptations. It is possible that in these cases the effect of the vegetation is indirect. *Culex poicilipes* larvae (Fig. 18a) have the ventral valves of the siphon greatly enlarged and have been observed to use these to trap bubbles of oxygen emitted by aquatic plants. *Hodgesia* larvae have the valves similarly modified. In *Culex argenteopunctatus* (Fig. 18b) the dorsal valves are provided with a stout spine, as also in *Aedeomyia* (Fig. 18c) and various species of *Ficalbia*. These spines serve for attachment, e.g., to the hydrofuge under surface of floating plants such as *Pistia*, with their trapped air film, or to masses of green alga. In both *C. poicilipes* and *C. argenteopunctatus*, as in *Aedeomyia*, there are tracheated bladder-like organs at the base of the antennae. Their function has not been adequately investigated but it is thought that they may serve for oxygen storage during the long period spent by such species on the bottom.

The extreme modification of the siphon found in *Mansonia* has already been noted (p. 79). Comparable modifications of a much less extreme kind are found in a few species of *Ficalbia* subgenus *Mimomyia* (Fig. 18d). Less specialized *Mimomyia* have strong spines on the dorsal, and long, flexible setae on the ventral, valves. In this respect they resemble larvae of subgenus *Ficalbia* specifically associated with horizontal vegetation (Fig. 18e). Larvae of the same subgenus associated with vertical vegetation show no such modification. Correlated with the character of the siphon valves are other characters affecting the comb teeth and pigmentation of the antenna.

Temporary Ground Pools

Extreme examples of this type of habitat are small rain pools on exposed rock or clay or in grassland, rice paddy or temporarily flooded pasture, drying up in a few days yet capable, in that time, of producing a huge population of adult mosquitoes. Habitats of this kind are available chiefly to aedine mosquitoes, some of which can complete their entire development from hatching to emergence in as little as four days or even slightly less. Among such species are *Ae.* (*Verrallina*) spp., breeding in flooded swamp forest, and *Ae.* (*Neomelaniconion*) spp. breeding in flooded grassland. A comparable species among the anophelines would be *An. gambiae,* which is said to be able to complete its development in about six days in exposed ground pools, often in clay and without vegetation.

Pools of the kind we have been discussing, if they remain water-filled for long enough, are likely to acquire an increasing proportion of *Culex* larvae. If they are in relatively open surroundings they may then act as important sources of vector species such as *C. tarsalis, C. tritaeniorhynchus, C. gelidus* and *C. annulirostris.* In forest the fauna will be a different one, but still a relatively generalized one. More specialized species will tend to appear if the dissolved organic matter accumulates beyond a certain point. Factors operating to exclude all but a few specialized species include high degrees of organic pollution, salinity, acidity and alkalinity. Acid habitats such as pools on sandy heaths are, by their nature, incompatible with agriculture and, in consequence, are seldom, if ever, productive of important disease vectors (though viable *C. p. fatigans* larvae have been found in a tank of hydrochloric acid with a pH of 1.5!). Extremes of alkalinity occur mainly in volcanic and desert regions and these also are incompatible with the production of disease vectors. Organic pollution may operate to exclude some vectors and dead vegetable matter has been used successfully for the control of anophelines. In general, however, species closely associated with man are, by the same token, tolerant of at least a moderate degree of pollution. *C. p. fatigans* is exceptional in being positively favoured by gross pollution but *C. tritaeniorhynchus, C. gelidus* and some *Mansonia* species also benefit from a moderate degree of pollution and their importance as vectors, in southern Asia, is often enhanced by the practice of manuring fish-ponds or ponds used for growing aquatic vegetation for animal fodder.

Brackish breeding places are found in estuaries, salt-marshes, mangrove swamps and coral or rock outcrops within range of wind-borne sea spray. They also occur in inland localities with natural salt deposits and in association with bodies of water such as desert oases or blocked lakes subject to a high degree of evaporation. Some anophelines, especially of Group *Pyretophorus,* are important malaria vectors in coastal areas. Examples are *An. sundaicus* and members of the *An. gambiae* complex. Salt-marsh species of *Aedes* (*Ochlerotatus*) are important nuisance mosquitoes and some North American ones may play a part in the transmission of encephalitis. *Ae. vigilax,* breeding in a variety of brackish pools, is an important vector of filariasis in New Caledonia. The *Culex annulirostris-sitiens* complex includes importance pest mosquitoes as well as vectors of Murray Valley encephalitis and, possibly, filariasis.

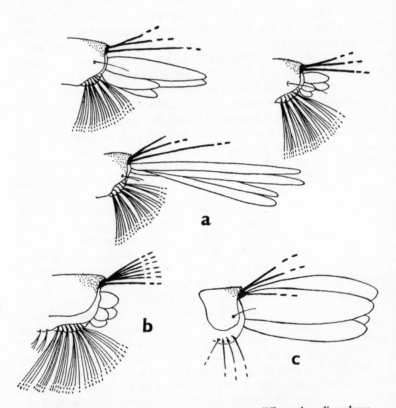

Fig. 19 Anal papillae. **a** *Culex decens* from three different breeding places. **b** *Ae. detritus,* showing the greatly reduced papillae characteristic of species breeding in brackish water. **c** *Ae.* (*Stegomyia*) *desmotes* showing the very large anal papillae sometimes found in container-breeders.

The anal papillae of freshwater larvae play an important part in the uptake of water and certain salts. Their shape and size vary in larvae reared in waters of varying degrees of salinity. They also vary as between species and between populations of the same species from different natural breeding places (Fig. 19a). In most brackish-water species they are reduced to small, globular structures which, in *Ae.* (*Ochl.*) *detritus* at least, are impermeable to water (Fig. 19b). In this species uptake of water and salts is confined to the gut.

Many aedine species breeding in ground pools have pectinate mouthbrush setae, as do many container-breeders. Larvae of *Opifex fuscus*, from seashore rock pools, are dimorphic in this respect, presumably as an adaptation to fuller exploitation of the breeding places by the employment of both filter-feeding and browsing (Fig. 20a, b). The effect is an environmental one and mouthbrushes of either type

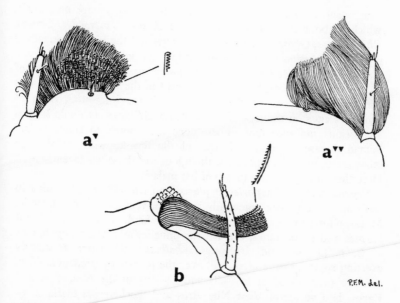

P.F.M. del.

Fig. 20 Larval mouthbrushes. **a′, a″** Mouthbrushe dimorphism in *Opifex fuscus*, arising as a direct response to availability of different-sized food particles and capable of modification from one instar to the next. **b** *Aedes* (*Mucidus*) sp. with mouthbrushes typical of those found in predatory culicine larvae.

can be induced in a given instar by providing food particles of appropriate size in the preceding instar. The response is not entirely uniform as between individuals, which may suggest a genetic polymorphism, though this has not been investigated. A similar dimorphism has been observed in some container-breeding *Aedes* and *Heizmannia*.

Facultative cannibalism seems to be commoner in container-breeding than in ground-pool species but several groups found only or mainly in ground pools are obligatory cannibals (*Psorophora* subgenus *Psorophora*, *Aedes* subgenus *Mucidus*, *Culex* subgenus *Lutzia*). In these the modifications associated with browsing (development of pectinate mouthbrush setae, reduction of antenna and antennal seta, reduction of maxillae, enlargement of mandibles) are all developed in an exaggerated degree (Fig. 20c).

Underground Habitats

The major class of breeding places in this category are crab-holes, which harbour specialized subgenera of *Aedes* (*Cancraedes*, *Skusea*, *Rhinoskusea*, *Geoskusea*, *Lorrainea*, *Levua*) and the highly specialized genus *Deinocerites*, as well as individual species of *Culex*, *Culiseta*, *Uranotaenia* and *Aedes* subgenus *Aedimorphus*. The larval biology of these species has been little studied except in the case of *Ae.* (*Skusea*) *pembaensis*, a vector of *Brugia patei* with the interesting habit of laying its eggs on the legs of crabs. Although some crab-hole species are serious nuisance mosquitoes, none are known to transmit any human disease. The same is true of the few known cavernicolous mosquitoes, mostly anophelines, though one of these has recently been incriminated in the transmission of bat malaria.

Species such as *Anopheles stephensi* and *An. claviger*, breeding in wells and cisterns, are potentially important vectors of urban malaria. More polluted breeding places of a similar kind, such as cesspits, pit latrines and septic tanks, can habour unbelievably dense populations of *C. p. fatigans* and *Armigeres subalbatus*, the latter apparently exerting some measure of control over the former by predation. *C. p.* var. *molestus*, breeding in wells and cisterns in the Near East and Egypt, is a vector of West Nile virus and wuchererian filariasis. In this area it also breeds readily above ground but further north it becomes obligatorily dependent on underground breeding places, at least during the winter, appearing from time to time as a serious nuisance mosquito during the summer.

Container Habitats

The whole of the Sabethini and Toxorhynchitini, at least 40 per cent of the Culicini and a negligible proportion of Anophelini occupy breeding places of this kind. Some authorities have argued that the Culicidae as a whole originated as container-breeders and there is much to be said for this point of view, though others argue to the contrary. It will be quite impossible to discuss container habitats in all their variety. We shall be able to deal only with some major features.

Two classes of tree-holes require to be distinguished, those found in certain waterside trees (phreatophytes) which are kept constantly filled by water drawn up by the roots and those which are directly dependent on rain. The former have been little studied though it seems that at least one species of North American *Orthopodomyia* is restricted to them. Other associations with particular types of tree probably exist but even less is known about these. As an example, *Stegomyia* species are entirely replaced by *Aedimorphus* in podocarp forests in East Africa.

Size of rot-hole, or at least of aperture, seems to be important in many cases. The very large horizontal rot-holes sometimes found in fallen trunks usually have a different fauna from smaller holes, with either vertical or horizontal aperture found in other situations. They are sometimes called log-holes to distinguish them. Tree-holes with very small apertures indeed are preferred by some sabethines (see Pl. IV). *Aedes* subgenus *Chaetocruiomyia* breed in very narrow tree-holes with apertures an inch or less in diameter, sometimes forming long pipes and located in very slender branches. The aspect of the aperture, whether vertical or horizontal, is important and some species will oviposit only in the one or the other. Horizontal apertures are precluded in the case of *S. chloropterus* by the mode of oviposition (p. 116).

Most, but not all, tree-hole-breeders have pectinate mouthbrush setae. Some species of *Heizmannia* and *Aedes* subgenus *Finlaya* exhibit a mouthbrush dimorphism recalling that found in *Opifex* (p. 79 and see Fig. 20, p. 93) but with the additional feature that the antennae also are dimorphic, being shorter in larvae with browsing mouthparts. The anal papillae are commonly very large and it has been suggested that this is related to the low chloride content of tree-hole water. Another common feature is the presence of large, multi-branched stellate setae on the thorax and abdomen. It has been suggested that these are protective against predation, or alternatively, that they help to keep the larvae from sinking into the deep layer of fine detritus commonly found at the bottom of tree-holes. In many *Stegomyia* larvae the extent to which such setae are developed varies with the tree-hole. In some, at least, it can be controlled in the laboratory by the use of extracts of water from particular tree-holes (Fig. 21a, b).

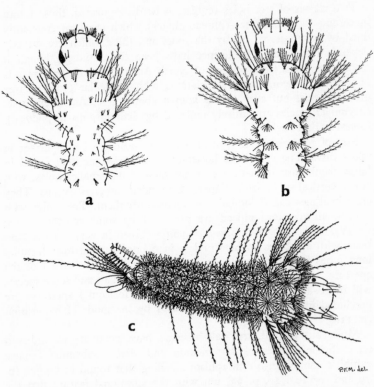

Fig. 21 a Larva of *Ae.* (*Stegomyia*) *albopictus* reared in hay infusion.
b The same reared in tree-hole water containing the 'hairiness factor' (see text). **c** Larva of *Tripteroides* sp. showing the condition found in most species of this genus

The effect is apparently dependent on the presence of finely divided, non-living, particulate matter suspended in the breeding water. Leaf-axils have the advantage over tree-holes of retaining water for remarkable lengths of time. In many cases the effect is enhanced by the ability of the larvae to burrow into the confined space at the base of the axil. Some larvae of this type can migrate to another axil if the water dries up.

Larvae of some *Topomyia*, breeding in leaf-axils, have stout spines on the maxillae and have been observed to prey on larvae of *Malaya*.

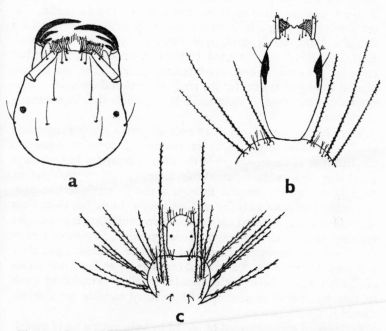

Fig. 22 Larvae from pitcher plants. **a** *Tripteroides filipes*, showing in an extreme form the great development of maxillary spines characteristic of the subgenus *Rachisoura*. These spines are probably associated mainly with necrophagy. **b** *Uranotaenia ascidiicola*, showing the reduction of antennae and head setae and, in an extreme form, the hypertrophy of the posterior part of the head capsule characteristic of many container-breeders. **c** *Tripteroides (Rachionotomyia) nepenthicola* with enlarged bases to the plueral seatae possibly serving for locomotion from one pitcher to another.

G

Larvae of *Tripteroides* subgenus *Rachisoura,* breeding in plant pitchers, have similar but larger spines and are thought to be either predatory or necrophagous (Fig. 22a).

Most axil-breeding species, other than those found in pitchers, lack stellate setae and these are conspicuously absent, for example, from some axil-breeding *Tripteroides* with close relatives of more normal kind breeding in tree-holes. Anopheline larvae are rarely found in axils. An interesting exception is *An. hackeri* (p. 43), breeding in leaft-bases of Nipa palms.

Bamboo habitats have many features of special ecological interest.[5] We can only deal with a few of them here. Erect bamboos bored by chrysomelid beetle larvae are particularly interesting. The fauna varies seasonally with the growth of the bamboos and with the enlargement of the bore-holes resulting from exodus of the mature beetles. Cut bamboos, presenting a horizontal aperture, generally support quite a different fauna as do dead, split bamboos lying on the ground. Artificially bored or transected bamboo internodes make excellent traps for a variety of container-breeding species. They can be suspended at various heights for the study of vertical distribution. Some species can be reared in them much more rapidly than in laboratory containers.

The decaying pulp of split cocoa pods supports a teeming population of *Eretmapodites* larvae. Split or rat-gnawed coconuts support a similar fauna of *Armigeres* while the pulp is decaying. In both cases the larvae swim with a remarkable vibratory 'shimmying' motion, possibly adaptive to progress through a viscous medium. Cut pawpaw stems may teem with *Culex* (*Culiciomyia*) larvae but these show less evidence of specialized adaptation. In coconuts there is progressive replacement by other mosquitoes (*Toxorhynchites, Stegomyia, Uranotaenia* spp.) as the organic content of the water diminishes and there is dilution by rainwater. Rat-gnawed coconuts are an important source of filariasis vectors belonging to the *Ae. scutellaris* complex, so much so that rat control is a recognized ancillary measure for filariasis control in the Pacific area.

Little useful purpose would be served by attempting a list of miscellaneous larval habitats. We shall merely mention as examples the cup fungi used by some *Finlaya* and the snail-shells which appear to be specifically attractive to certain *Eretmapodites*. It is nearly true to say that 'if it holds water mosquitoes will breed in it somewhere or other'. The outstanding exception is the very large container, such as a tank or reservoir, with absolutely clean edges.

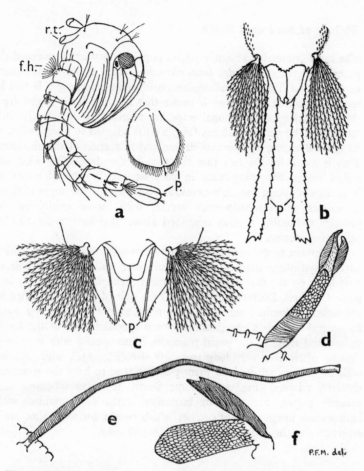

P.F.M. del.

Fig. 23 Culicine and sabethine pupae. **a** Generalized culicine pupa. **b, c** Terminal segments and paddles, **b** *Ficalbia* (*Ravenalites*) sp., **c** *Topomyia* sp. **d, e, f** Respiratory trumpets, **d** *Mansonia* (*Mansonioides*) sp., **e** *Ficalbia* (*Ravenalites*) sp., **f** *Hodgesia* sp. Although subgenus *Ravenalites* are container-breeders (mainly in leaf-axils, including the very large ones of *Ravenala*), the trumpets and paddles recall those of other *Ficalbia* breeding in dense aquatic vegetation. *In Hodgesia* and some *Anopheles* the trumpet is provided with a tragus which is erected by the pull of the surface film on its hydrophil outer wall when at the surface. *Mansonia* spp. have the trumpets modified for piercing, as with the larval siphon. The paddles recall those of *Ficalbia*.

Biology of the Pupal Stage

The most interesting recent work on pupal biology has concerned the pupation rhythm in *Aedes taeniorhynchus*. This, however, is related to the periodicity and synchronization of adult emergence. It will be more convenient to discuss it under that heading later. Apart from this the biology of the pupal stage has received comparatively little attention. The general habitus (Fig. 23a) is adapted to progression, in an upward zigzag by alternate flexion and relaxation of the abdomen. This is aided by the fact that the tarsi of the developing adult are coiled under the wing-cases in contrast to all other families of Nematocera except the Chironomidae. As an exception, pupae of those *Armigeres* and *Eretmapodites* species with larvae exhibiting the peculiar swimming motion described above also have a comparable swimming motion.

Attachment to the surface film is by the respiratory trumpets, which have a hydrofuge inner and hydrophil outer wall, and by a pair of float hairs on the first abdominal segment (vestigial in *Mansonia* and some *Ficalbia*). Locomotion is aided by a pair of paddles attached to the eighth abdominal segment (much reduced in Sabethini, Fig. 23c). In general there is a correlation between specializations of the larval siphon and those of the pupal trumpets. Thus species with very long siphons often have very long trumpets also (Fig. 23e), while species with the siphon adapted for plant-piercing tend to have the trumpets similarly adapted (Fig. 23d). Some South American sabethine and culicine pupae, occurring in bromeliad axils, are provided with luminescent integumentary patches which persist for some time after emergence of the adult. Their function is unknown.

REFERENCES

1. BATES, M., 1949, *The Natural History of Mosquitoes*. New York: MacMillan.
2. LAIRD, M., 1956, *Studies of Mosquitoes and Fresh water Ecology in the South Pacific*. Wellington: Royal Society of New Zealand.
3. HOPKINS, G. H. E., 1952, *Mosquitoes of the Ethiopian Region*. Vol. I. 2nd Edn. London: British Museum (Natural History).

4. THOMSON, R. C. M., 1951, *Mosquito Behaviour in Relation to Malaria Transmission and Control in the Tropics.* London: Arnold.

5. MACDONALD, W. W., 1960, *Malaysian Parasites.* XXXVIII. *On the Systematics and Ecology of* Armigeres *subgenus* Leicesteria (*Diptera, Culicidae*). Kuala Lumpur: Institute of Medical Research.

VII

Mosquito Biology: the Adults

ALTHOUGH it is natural to think of adult mosquitoes in terms of a widely dispersed population, the impression is to some extent illusory. At many, if not, indeed, at all, times during the lives of the individuals which compose them, mosquito populations show a tendency to cohere. The effect is particularly marked in relation to certain activities. We shall consider these in approximately the order in which they occur during the life of the mosquito.

Emergence and dispersal

A necessary prelude to the emergence of the adult is the rupture of the trachea leading from the pupal trumpets. This permits the accumulation of air below the pupal exuvium. At the same time air is swallowed, the stomach is distended, the pupal exuvium splits along the mid-dorsal line of the cephalothorax and the emerging adult is forced vertically upwards through the resultant slit. The pressure of air in the stomach also serves to expand the wings and legs and after a few minutes the adult is able to leave the surface of the water and fly for a short distance. A resting period follows during which the wings and legs harden and the male hypopygium rotates through 180°. The majority of males develop more rapidly than the females in both the larval and the pupal stages and, consequently, emerge first.

In *Aedes taeniorhynchus* well-marked emergence peaks are discernible each day. The duration of the pupal stage is governed mainly by temperature and is independent of photoperiod. Synchronism of emergence must, therefore, reflect a corresponding synchronization of times of pupation. The latter, in turn, is governed by an internal 'clock' of a kind which we shall describe in more detail later. In constant darkness peaks of pupation occur with a periodicity of about 21.5 hours. Exposure to light for four hours, followed by return to continuous darkness, or exposure to alternating twelve-hour periods of light and dark, sharpens the pupation peaks and lengthens the interval between them to about 22.3 hours. (A temperature cue of a similar kind, or exposure to alternating periods of high and low temperature, has the same effect.) Stress resulting from overcrowding coupled with restricted food-supply and high salinity in the breeding place lengthens the interval to the extent that the pupation rhythm may assume an exact twenty-four-hour periodicity. Such conditions must frequently be encountered in nature by salt-marsh species such as *Ae. taeniorhynchus.*

Dispersal has been studied chiefly by the recapture of marked mosquitoes emanating from known release points. Marking techniques include the use of small spots of paint, employing a colour and position code to distinguish individual releases, and the use of radioactive isotopes. The latter are administered to the larvae, thus obviating the necessity for any handling of the adults. The presence of tagged individuals can be detected either by the use of a Geiger-Müller tube or by autoradiography, using X-ray film (Pl. XII, p. 169). The latter method has the advantage that different releases can be distinguished by the use of isotopes with varying penetrating power.[1]

Exodus from the vicinity of the breeding places (see Pl. VI) is a true migration in the sense previously defined (p. 49). Feeding associated with growth takes place only in the larval stage. Meals taken by the adult are devoted either to the production of energy for flight or to the maturation of the eggs. The essential requirement for flight is a supply of glycogen. This can be accumulated with great rapidity from a sugar meal. A single meal of this kind may suffice for flights up to 50 km.[2] Storage of glycogen derived from a blood-meal is much slower. Adults of both sexes of *Ae. taenirohynchus* have been observed to feed on mangrove flowers prior to their extensive disperal flights (up to twenty-five miles or more).[3] In *Anopheles gambiae,* on the other hand, two blood-meals are commonly taken before maturation of the first egg-batch and it has been suggested that the first of these may provide energy for the exodus flight.

Dispersal seems seldom to be random. The factors governing direction are probably complex but, in general, mosquitoes show a tendency to fly up-wind in gentle air currents. Strong winds inhibit flight and down-wind flights occur with wind-speeds of moderate strength. Very extensive wind-assisted flights seem sometimes to occur. *Ae. (Ochl.) sollicitans* have been encountered more than 100 miles off-shore and there is evidence for even more extensive flights under special meteorological conditions. (See also p. 75.) Salt-marsh species,

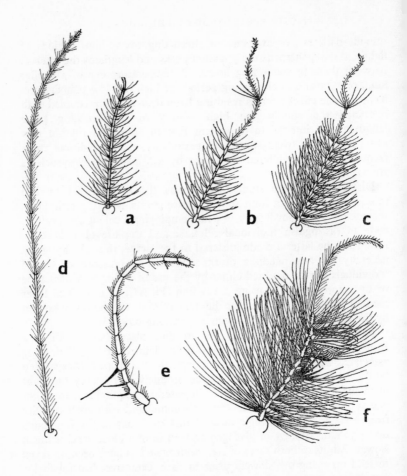

Fig. 24 Male antennae. **a** *Wyeomyia mystes*. In this, as in many other sabethines, the male antennae are only slightly more plumose than in the female. Less usual is the absence of any elongation of the terminal segments. **b** *Heizmannia scintillans*. Reduced plumosity is characteristic of this genus, as of some other quasi-sabethines, but the males remain recognizable by the elongated terminal segments. **c** *Heizmannia achaetae*, annectent in many respects between *Aedes* and more typical *Heizmannia*. **d, e** *Deinocerites epitedeus* and *Opifex fuscus*, members of highly specialized genera for which see text. **f** *Culex (Lophoceraomyia) cinctellus*. Members of this subgenus have densely plumose antennae, though less so than in some *Aedes*. In addition many species have elaborate tufts of modified scales on several segments, the function of which is entirely unknown.

in general, have notably long flight ranges but in *Opifex*, breeding on rocky seashores, the wing-beat is exceptionally slow and there are other features possibly associated with the need to avoid being blown out to sea. Forest mosquitoes appear to have more restricted flight ranges than those breeding in open situations. This may be true of container-breeders in general. Special conditions prevail in the case of urban species such as *Ae. aegypti* and *C p. fatigans* but the dispersal of these has only recently begun to be effectively studied.[4]

Swarming and Mating

Mating behaviour has been studied in greatest detail in *Ae. aegypti*.[5] As to how far, and in what sense, this species can be taken as representative is an open question. Coupling appears to take place chiefly, though not exclusively, on the wing and to be completed at rest. Females appear to show little preference as between males. Copulation leads to insemination only when the females have reached a certain age, the length of the refractory period varying from about one to two days depending on strain and pre-mating temperature. Small male swarms are formed in nature but they are not essential as a prelude to mating which will take place in extremely confined spaces, for which reason the species is said to be stenogamous. Pheromones have not been demonstrated in *Ae. aegypti*, though male stimulants are said to be secreted by females of *Culiseta inornata* and there is evidence for the production of male attractants by females of *Culex pipiens* and *C. tarsalis*. Experimental evidence leaves little doubt that, in *Ae. aegypti*, the essential prelude to mating is the reception of auditory stimuli produced by movements of the female wings, not necessarily in flight. Reception of these stimuli is by Johnston's organ and is enhanced by the erectile hairs on the densely-plumose male antennae. The great variation found in these organs is doubtless reflected in a wide spectrum of mating behaviour throughout the group (Fig. 24). *Ae. aegypti* may be conjectured to lie somewhere near the middle of this spectrum, with respect to its mating behaviour, showing neither the highly specialized behaviour or *Opifex* and *Deinocerites*, in which mating is initiated during emergence from the pupa, nor the extensive swarm-formation characteristic of strongly flying species in which quite extensive mating is apparently achieved even after exodus and dispersal.

In *Opifex* detection of the pupa is visual. The males spend much of their time on the water surface and have been observed, at times, to thrust their heads below the water. The pupae are detected both directly and by the ripples which they create when surfacing. The pupa is grasped initially with the large fore tarsal claws and subsequently with the claspers (Fig. 25a).

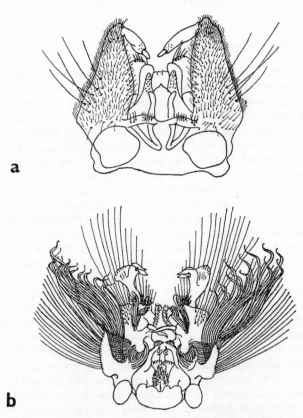

Fig. 25 Male terminalia. **a** *Opifex fuscus*, with terminalia of a relatively simple type. **b** *Heizmannia covelli*, showing the great complexity achieved in some sabethine and quasi-sabethine genera. The functional significance of this complexity is unknown but it has been observed that in *Eretmapodites chrysogaster* coupling on the wing is followed by copulation at rest, sometimes lasting for more than an hour during which the male hangs head-downwards 'quivering rapidly and violently throughout'.

As soon as emergence begins the terminalia are inserted into the pupal skin. Emerging males are rejected when the two hypopygia come into contact. Females emerging unmated may be mated either on the water surface or in flight a short distance above it.

In *Deinocerites cancer* mating takes place in the virtual darkness of the crab-hole in which emergence takes place. Detection of the female appears to be by chemical stimuli operating over 1-2 cm. prior to emergence or 10-15 cm. when emergence begins. Mating activity of the male is also elicited by contact with resting mosquitoes of either sex. Once located the female pupa is frequently held by the trumpet with the claws of one fore tarsus and sensed with the abnormally long antennae (Fig. 24e, p. 104 and see Pl. V, p. 120). Small swarms of other *Deinocerites* species have been seen at the mouths of crab-holes at dusk and mating has been observed at this time though it is not clear whether it originated in the swarms. In *Deinocerites pseudes*, the only other species colonized, males mate with resting females after emergence of the latter. In *Deinocerites*, as in *Opifex*, the hypopygium is relatively simple but it differs from those of all other mosquitoes in having the lobes of the ninth tergite enlarged and articulated.

Opifex and *Deinocerites* are the only genera in which mating is known to take place during emergence. In many others, however, (*Ficalbia, Uranotaenia, Mansonia, Culiseta, Aedes, Psorophora, Culex*) mating has been observed in the immediate vicinity of the breeding places, much of it presumably involving recently emerged females. At the same time there is good evidence that, in many species, quite extensive mating takes place after dispersal. In *Anopheles gambiae* mating has been shown to take place both before and after the first blood-meal. In *An. stephensi* it has been shown to involve parous females. In *Ae. taeniorhynchus* extensive mating takes place at the time of the exodus from the breeding areas but, at this time, many males are still too young so that a significant proportion of mating must take place after dispersal. Mating in *Anopheles sundaicus* has been observed two miles from the nearest breeding place.

Various factors operate to minimize the effect of dispersal in reducing contact between the sexes. In many cases both sexes share preferred types of resting place. In others (some species of *Aedes* and *Psorophora*), males have been observed to congregate in the vicinity of the host and mate with the females as they come to feed. In some *Aedes* (*Ochlerotatus, Diceromyia*), *Psorophora, Eretmapodites* and *Mansonia*, mating takes place at this time not only on the wing but while the females are actually engorging.

Such situations are, however, by no means universal. It seems that, in many cases at least, an essential requirement for mating after dispersal is the formation of male swarms. The characteristic feature of such swarms is that they form and maintain station in relation to a marker which may be anything from a patch of discoloured earth to the head of the observer, a chimney-pot or the top of a tree. They range in size from small groups, e.g. of *Aedes aegypti* swarming over pieces of furniture in a room, to vast clouds of *Ochlerotatus* species swarming above the tree-tops. In spite of some suggestions to the contrary, there is no reason to suppose that the behaviour involved in these extreme examples is essentially different or that the very large swarms owe their special character to anything other than the large numbers involved, coupled, perhaps, with some consequent hyper-excitation of the males. Nor has it been demonstrated that male swarms play a significant role in the life of the mosquito except in relation to mating.

Attempts have been made to minimize the extent to which mating takes place in these swarms and to stress the small numbers of females which are commonly caught or observed in them. There are, however, factors which tend to create a false impression in this respect, such as the fact that swarming is usually associated with morning or evening twilight, when direct observation is difficult, while, in general, copula-tion, though initated in the swarm, is completed outside it. It must also be remembered that the number of copulations will mainly reflect the number of available females and so must be expected to vary widely according to circumstances. Individual males swarm repeatedly and the number of copulations is, accordingly, cumulative. It has been estimated that in some swarms of *Ae. (Ochl.) hexodontus* the rate of entry of females into the swarm is sufficient to permit mating of all the males involved in about six hours, i.e. in rather less than the total swarming time on two successive days. Still greater swarming rates have been reported for *An. stephensi*, particularly when swarming immediately after release so that an abundance of females was available.

Attraction of the female into the swarm has been generally supposed to be visual, though recent indications of the secretion of pheromones by mosquitoes (p. 105) have prompted the suggestion that, in the case or large swarms at least, it may be olfactory. Males of different species have characteristic wing-beat frequencies and the noise of a small swarm, if recorded and played back, is highly attractive but only to other males. Female swarms have seldom been observed but they have been recorded in *Culex pipiens fatigans* and *Aedes hexodontus*. In the latter case a small female swarm was observed to form in relation to

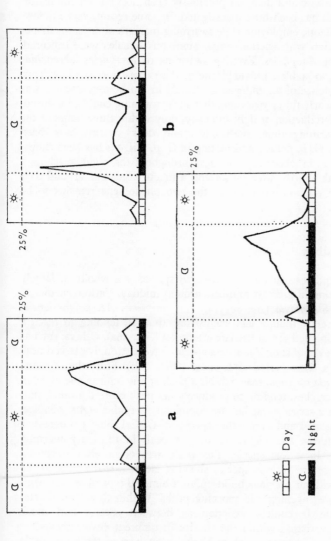

Fig. 26 24-hour biting cycles: **a** *Aedes aegypti*, **b** *Aedes africanus*, **c** *Anopheles gambiae*. These are a simple record of hourly totals of mosquitoes coming to feed on human bait, summed over a series of catches. The term 'biting cycle' implies no more than this. It does not, for example, imply that there is a corresponding cyclical variation in the urge to bite. They could be no more than activity cycles, representing variations in the probability of making contact with the bait. (**a** based on McClelland, *Bull. ent. Res.*, **50**: 687, 1960; **b** and **c** based on Mattingly, *ibid.*, **40**: 149, 1949).

Day

Night

the same marker as the male swarm but nearer to the ground. It is possible that females are more commonly attracted to the same markers as the males than has previously been noticed but the matter is one which has been little investigated. In some recent, very interesting experiments, employing male swarming markers of different shapes in conjunction with suction traps, numerous females were captured, especially of *Anopheles*. Evening swarming of *Anopheles labranchiae atroparvus*, in stables, provided one of the earliest pieces of evidence for the existence of an endogenous 'clock' in mosquitoes when it was observed, nearly thirty years ago, that such swarming could be induced, by artificial reduction of light intensity, only within three hours of the normal swarming time. Both dawn and dusk swarms have been observed in *C. p. pallens* and mating in *C. p. fatigans* has been shown to take place, in laboratory colonies, throughout the night, reaching a smaller peak shortly after sunset and a much larger one around daybreak. The relationship between the two phenomena remains to be established.

Blood-feeding

Some mosquitoes, such as *Haemagogus* species, are wholly or largely diurnal, biting in greatest numbers around midday. Various medically important *Stegomyia* (*Ae. aegypti, Ae. simpsoni, Ae. polynesiensis*) are also largely, though less exclusively, diurnal, tending to reach a peak of biting activity in the late afternoon (Fig. 26a). Others, such as *Ae. africanus, and* some *Mansonia* species have a strongly marked peak occupying a short period after sunset (Fig. 26b). Still other species, e.g. *Mansonia africana,* may exhibit a peak at any hour of the night in individual catches, tending to produce a flat peak centred around midnight when a series of catches are combined. Yet others (*An. gambiae, An. balabacensis* and some other species of *Cellia*) show a progressive build-up during the night, reaching a peak in the early morning (Fig. 26c). In a few species this peak may occur after daybreak. Finally there are various species showing either a sharp peak in the morning, without previous build-up, or a bimodal type of activity with roughly equal evening and morning peaks. Within these broad categories there is endless variation as between species and much interesting variation within the species in different environments.[6]

The logical point at which to begin an analysis of the biting cycle would seem to be the initation of flight activity leading eventually to the location of the host. For purposes of discussion we shall confine ourselves to mosquitoes which customarily rest during the daytime, becoming active around the time of sunset. These are the most thoroughly studied. There is little direct evidence linking flight activity with biting activity in the species with which we shall be concerned, but in an interesting recent study, employing a sweep-net mounted on the roof of a car, it was shown that flight activity in *Aedes vexans* has a bimodal periodicity, with evening and morning peaks showing a general correspondence with the bimodal biting activity.

Particular interest attaches to the part played, in initiating nocturnal activity, by the type of endogenous 'clock' whose role in pupation rhythms we already noted (p. 102). This has been studied in *Culex pipiens*, by means of an actograph, and in *Anopheles gambiae*, using an automatic sound-recording technique. We shall briefly describe the results of the work on *An. gambiae* as an example of the mode of operation of 'clocks' in general. Analogies with the pupation rhythm in *Ae. taeniorhynchus* will be apparent.

The essential fact to grasp, and the one which causes most confusion in the minds of those unfamiliar with the subject, is that 'clocks' of the kind we are discussing are to some extent permissive in their action rather than instructive. That is to say they prescribe when an activity may be performed, other things being equal. They do not instruct an animal that an activity must be performed at a certain time whatever the environmental conditions. It follows that the only certain proof, or disproof, of the existence of a 'clock' lies in the repetition, or non-repetition, of a particular activity at approximately twenty-four-hour (circadian) intervals in a constant environment. In *An. gambiae* the onset of nocturnal activity is dependent on the disappearance of light. There will be no such onset so long as the light remains constant, whatever the 'clock' may say. On the other hand, neither will there be a response to the 'light off' signal if this is administered at a time during the twenty-four hours other than that prescribed by the 'clock'. In *An. gambiae* no activation by a 'light off' signal takes place unless this is administered twenty-one hours or more after the previous change from light to dark, i.e., in the case of mosquitoes kept in a twelve hour light – twelve hour dark regime, three hours before the end of the light period. Even after twenty-one hours the response to the change to darkness is very slow, activation taking nearly three hours. As the end of the twenty-four hours is approached, the response speeds up and activation eventually takes only a few minutes. It is never instantaneous, however, which suggests that the underlying mechanism of activation is probably hormonal rather than neural. Under conditions of constant darkness following on the administration of a suitable light cue (see p. 118) there is, of course, no inhibitory effect of light. In these circumstances activation recurs with a periodicity of approximately twenty-three hours, much as with the pupation rhythm in *Ae. taeniorhynchus*.

A glance at Fig. 26c will show that, while the 'clock' may assist in determining the time of onset of biting activity, it can have little to do with the shape subsequently assumed by the biting curve. Nor can the progressive increase in activity throughout the hours of darkness be attributed to changes in environmental conditions, since it is precisely at this time that such conditions are most constant. Rather, it seems, we must look at a combination of factors, possibly involving quite diverse aspects of the life of the mosquito. Among those factors most likely to be involved would seem to be readiness to feed at particular times, about which we shall have more to say later (p. 119) and, perhaps, variations in the pattern of alternate flight and rest, among them the quite long period of rest in the immediate vicinity of the host, prior to feeding, now known to characterize a number of species.

Whatever the underlying factors, the biting cycles of many species are so constant in different, but comparable, situations as clearly to reflect basic patterns of behaviour and general biology specific to the species in question and of fundamental importance in their lives (Fig. 27a, b). In some cases, also, drastic changes take place when the biting cycle is recorded in a sharply differing environment (Fig. 27c). An understanding of the way in which such changes are brought about would almost certainly continute significantly to our understanding of aspects of behaviour important for epidemiological assessment and control.

We shall not attempt any detailed discussion of the factors involved in host-location. They are complex and still very little understood. Some believe that the initial arrival in the vicinity of the host is random, others that it results from long-distance attraction. Olfactory attraction is theoretically feasible up to about a mile. Mosquitoes have been shown to fly up-wind, in moderate air currents, in response to visual stimuli. Some form of visual orientation at night is possible, in theory, since they are sensitive to light intensities down to about one-quarter normal starlight while there is evidence to suggest that certain anophelines, at least, fly low over the ground at night. Carbon dioxide, in moderate concentrations, is highly stimulatory and, it seems, attractive. (In stronger concentrations it is a useful anaesthetic.) 'Dry ice' is often used in traps alone or as an adjuvant to bait.

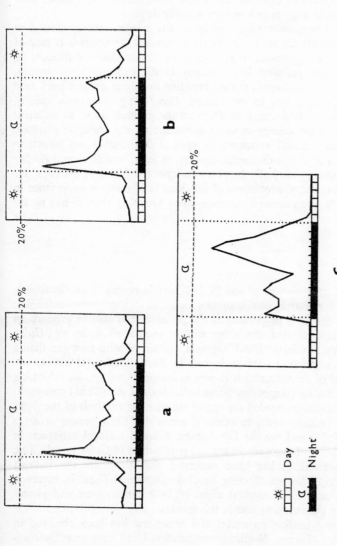

Fig. 27 Biting cycles of *Mansonia fuscopennata* in Uganda. **a** At the foot of the steel tower in forest at Mpanga. **b** The same at Zika (see Pl. VII). **c** In house, Zika. Not only is the biting cycle similar in the first two cases but in both a closely similar series of changes takes place while ascending the tower (ref. 7, p. 124). *M. uniformis* has a similar type of biting cycle in Malaya and this also shows striking changes in the biting cycle in houses (ref. 5, p. 82). (After Haddow, *Trans. R. ent. Soc. Lond.*, **113**: 315; 1961).

Temperature and humidity gradients may play a part in the final descent on the host. Summarizing, it is probably fair to say that there is a great deal of evidence as to how mosquitoes might locate their hosts, almost none as to how they actually do so.

Forest mosquitoes vary widely in the heights above ground at which they mainly feed. The factor of vertical distribution is thus of considerable importance in relation to the transmission of diseases of, e.g., arboreal primates living mostly in the canopy. Some species, such as *Aedes africanus*, though breeding mainly at ground-level, feed in greatest numbers in the canopy. Others, e.g. *Mansonia* species, though biting in greatest numbers on the ground, do so in sufficient numbers in the canopy to serve as vectors of, e.g., brugian filariasis. Daily and seasonal variations in vertical distribution are known to occur and it seems that some species, at least, which ascend readily into the canopy may also be prone to leave the forest, at intervals, for the open country. Movement of this kind is of obvious importance in relation to zoonosis and deserves more attention than it has so far received.

Sugar-feeding

As we already saw (p. 75 and Pl. IV), certain genera (*Toxorhynchites, Malaya*) are entirely unable to take blood. In various species belonging to other genera a proportion of the population is able to produce an egg-batch, of limited size, either without food at all, as in, e.g., *Culex pipiens* var. *molestus* and *Wyeomyia smithii*, or with no more than a meal of sugar or nectar as in certain Arctic *Aedes* (*Ochlerotatus*). This type of reproduction is known as autogeny and species exhibiting it are said to be autogenous. Some individuals of *Ae.* (*Ochl.*) *communis* obtain substances needed for egg-maturation by autolysis of the flight muscles. In most cases, however, it seems that the necessary reserves are carried over from the larval stage. Marked seasonal variations in the incidence of autogeny in natural populations of *Culex tarsalis* have been observed. It has been suggested that these are the indirect expression of factors affecting larval development. There is, however, also evidence for a marked effect of both temperature and photo-period on the autogeny rate in this species.

Extensive feeding on nectar and honeydew has been observed in both sexes of some Northern mosquitoes. Until very recently comparable behaviour had been observed mainly in males in the tropics. Latterly, however, both sexes of more than thirty species have been found feeding on flowers and extra-floral nectar sources in Uganda, *Hodgesia* spp. being particularly abundant. In addition both sexes of *Anopheles aquasalis* have been found feeding on flowers in Trinidad and both sexes of *Culex pipiens fatigans* were shown to feed extensively on sugar-cane trash in Rangoon. A twice-daily sugar-feeding rhythm has been recorded in *Aedes aegypti* in the laboratory, by measuring the depletion of a glucose/sucrose solution at four-hourly intervals The rhythm became unimodal when the mosquitoes were maintained in continuous darkness and this was taken to suggest the operation of an internal 'clock'. Marking of a variety of flowers with radioactive tracers, in the Siwa oasis, showed that males, at least, are relatively specific in their choice of flowers.

Oviposition

It was at one time widely believed that mosquitoes, other than container-breeders, scattered their eggs at random on the wing and that the association of particular species with particular types of breeding place was due to differential survival of the larvae. Such beliefs are entirely contrary to those held today. It is true that some anophelines are more prone to scatter their eggs widely while flying over a breeding place than are others. This does not, however, in itself imply a lack of discrimination in the choice of oviposition sites. Recent studies have invariably tended to show that the minutiae of oviposition behaviour are both complex and very highly specific indeed (ref. 4, p. 101).

That female mosquitoes normally employ oviposition sites adapted to the requirements of the larvae need not, of course, imply parental foresight. Ovipositing females of some arctic *Ochlerotatus* are attracted exclusively to the most strongly insolated parts of the pools round which they lay. The fact that it is these parts which will first become ice-free the following year, to the advantage of the larvae, does not imply foresight though it may have influenced the evolution of the parental behaviour. Various physical factors affect the choice of oviposition site. Recognition of unacceptable salinity or pollution levels is apparently achieved through tarsal chemoreceptors. Attraction, in the case of species favouring polluted breeding sites, is presumably similarly mediated. It has recently been shown that suspensions of bacteria (*Aerobacter aerogenes*) from hay infusions may be even more attractive to *C. p. fatigans* than the hay infusions themselves.

Brackish-water habitats present a special problem since several species laying wholly or largely in breeding places of this type in the field show a decided preference for freshwater, in which to oviposit, when offered a choice in the laboratory. In most laboratory tests, however, the only salt employed has been sodium chloride which may not be the most important constituent in natural breeding waters. Calcium sulphate has been shown to be strongly attractive to *Anopheles labranchiae atroparvus* though, in a recent study, *Ae. nigromaculis* and *Ae. dorsalis* failed to show any marked discrimination as between NaCl and $CaCl_2$, while differing sharply in their reaction to KCl. In the course of these experiments it was observed that heavy mortality among *Ae. nigromaculis* eggs ensued when these were laid on soil moistened with NaCl solution, 1 per cent Cl being about the highest concentration tolerated. *Ae. dorsalis*, on the other hand, could tolerate salinities up to at least 2.5 per cent Cl. It is suggested that this might partly explain the more restricted range of breeding sites occupied by *Ae. nigromaculis* (a revival, in another form, of early selective mortality theories). In the *An. gambiae* complex, neither differences in salt-tolerance nor differences in the reactions of ovipositing females seem capable of explaining the most complete mutual exclusion of brackish and freshwater forms from one another's breeding sites. Differences in substrate have been cited as a possible cause, the pools in mangrove swamp generally used by *An. melas* having a much darker bottom than those favoured by freshwater *An. gambiae*. Various species of mosquitoes have been shown to oviposit preferentially on dark substrates.

Visual stimuli may well be of major importance in the case of tree-hole breeders. *Sabethes chloropterus* lays its eggs mainly in tree-holes with large cavities but very small apertures (Pl. IV). In the laboratory, bamboo sections with holes bored in the vertical sides are acceptable but those cut across so as to provide a horizontal aperture are not. This is related to the mode of oviposition whereby the abdomen is tucked forward between the legs, while the insect is hovering in front of the aperture, and the eggs are projected horizontally for distances up to 10 c.m. *Toxorhynchites* species breeding in beetle-bored bamboos probably behave similarly since the bore-holes are too small to admit these mosquitoes. Some bamboo-breeders have the thorax laterally compressed and can enter very small holes indeed.

Tactile stimuli are important to *Aedes* species laying in containers and to species of this genus and *Psorophora* laying in depressions in the ground. In the laboratory such species show a marked perference for rough surfaces offering an approximation to the minute crevices into which the eggs are inserted in nature. *Ps. ferox* was found to lay readily on damp filter-paper placed on top of the cage while ignoring similar paper placed on the floor. This behaviour caused considerable puzzlement until it was realized that the gauze forming the top of the cage afforded small crannies smiliar to those used in nature. There is no evidence of either positive or negative geotaxy in species of this kind, but strongly marked positive geotaxy has been demonstrated in gravid females of the *Culex pipiens* complex leading to preferential oviposition at ground-level.[4] High moisture-content is conducive to species such as *Ae. taeniorhynchus* laying on damp soil, but it seems probable that this is sensed as atmospheric humidity immediately above the soil surface rather than directly.

Marginal vegetation at the edge of an oviposition site is attractive to anophelines such as *An. minimus* which commonly breed along stream edges. This species can detect currents with velocity as low as 0.05 feet per second (ref. 4, p. 101). In the case of *An. gambiae*, breeding in exposed ground pools, it is strongly deterrent, the direct effect of exposure to sunlight being less important than its indirect effect in destroying marginal vegetation. Oviposition by *An. culicifacies* in rice-fields has been found to cease when the growing plants reach a height of about a foot. Glass rods planted vertically exert a similar deterrent effect on this species.

Oviposition Cycles

Much of our knowledge of the endogenous element in cyclical behaviour has come from studies of this kind.[8] When maintained in a twelve hour light – twelve hour dark regime *Aedes aegypti* shows a strongly marked oviposition peak shortly before the end of the light period (Fig. 28s). So long as the mosquitoes are maintained in alternating dark and light periods (not necessarily of equal length) regular cycling continues. When they are reared and maintained in continuous light or continuous darkness it fails to develop. The essential requirement to initiate cycling is a change from light to darkness (the so-called 'light cue', see p. 118). Exposure to light for as little as five seconds is sufficient to establish a rhythm which will persist for four-five days in continuous darkness (Fig. 28c).

The oviposition cycle of *Aedes africanus*, as recorded in the laboratory, resembles that of *Ae. aegypti* but with the main peak somewhat shallower and occurring nearer the time of sunset. A similar peak is encountered in nature when the eggs are laid in forest, but outside the forest oviposition is delayed until after sunset. It seems, therefore,

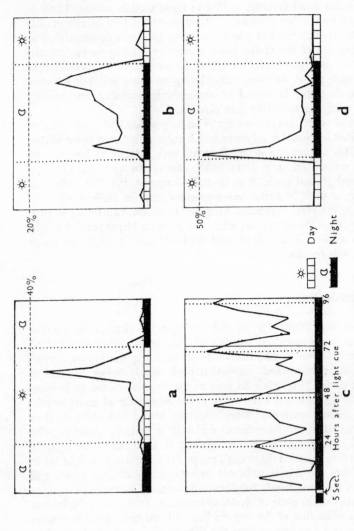

Fig. 28 Oviposition cycles. **a** *Aedes aegypti* maintained in a natural 12 hour light—12 hour dark regime in the laboratory. **b** *Mansonia fuscopennata* in a similar regime. **c** *Ae. aegypti* maintained in continuous darkness after receiving a five-second light cue. **d** *Anopheles gambiae* in natural 12 hour light—12 hour dark regime. (Broken vertical lines show anticipated times of peaks). (After Haddow et al., *Ann. trop. Med. Parasit.*, **51**: 159, 1957, **52**: 320, 1958, **55**: 427, 1961 and **56**: 352, 1962 respectively).

that this species is inhibited more strongly by light than *Ae. aegypti*. In contrast to this, a third species of *Stegomyia*, *Ae. apicoargenteus*, shows a poorly defined peak, in the laboratory, early in the afternoon. In the field the oviposition cycle of this species varies seasonally, resembling the laboratory cycle initially but becoming bimodal, with morning and afternoon peaks, as the weather becomes hotter and drier.

Among nocturnal species *An. gambiae* has been studied only in the laboratory, where it shows a well-marked oviposition peak in the early evening (Fig. 28d) contrasting sharply with its main biting peak in the early morning (Fig. 26c, p. 109). It has seemed a reasonable supposition that the morning biting peak, otherwise difficult to explain, might reflect the contribution made by females ovipositing in the early evening and feeding again the same night. Recent evidence, however, suggests that the proportion doing this may not be very large.[9]

In *Mansonia fuscopennata* the situation is reversed. In this species the main biting peak occurs shortly after sunset (Fig. 27a, b, p. 113), but the main oviposition peak is delayed until the early morning (Fig. 28b). It is suggested that, in this case, the main evening biting peak may involve females which oviposited before daybreak earlier on the same day, while the smaller morning biting peak may involve mosquitoes which oviposited at the time of the small evening oviposition peak the day before. Some support for this hypothesis is provided by the fact that parous females make up a roughly constant proportion (40-50 per cent) of *M. fuscopennata* feeding at different times of the night. Later work showed, however, that many females contributing to the post-sunset biting peak had oviposited thirty-six hours or more before coming to feed.

C. p. fatigans exhibits a strongly-marked oviposition peak shortly after the onset of dark when it is kept in a twelve hour light-twelve hour dark regime in the laboratory. A similar peak is encountered under undisturbed conditions in the field and this is matched by the well-marked activity peak revealed by actograph studies, in controlled regimes in the laboratory in *C. pipiens pallens*. Interestingly both the oviposition cycle and the activity cycle show a strong tendency to bimodality with a secondary peak occurring just before or after the onset of the light period. (This also appears in the activity cycle of *An. gambiae* and seems to be a common feature of many cycles recorded in the field.) There is some evidence for a differential contribution to the morning and evening peaks by mosquitoes previously fed during the earlier and later part of the night respectively.[4] However, more work needs to be done with this species in controlled regimes.

There are some grounds for supposing that circadian rhythms may play a less important part in the lives of species occurring in more northerly latitudes than is the case with tropical species such as those we have been discussing. It is claimed that, in the laboratory, *Culex tarsalis* shows twin oviposition peaks during the first hour of light and the first hour of darkness respectively. These peaks are said to be independent of any prior light cue and to be completely suppressed when the mosquitoes are transferred from alternating light and dark into continuous light or darkness.

Oviposition and biting cycles, as ordinarily studied, are population phenomena. The contribution of individual mosquitoes to the oviposition cycle has been studied with single pairs of *Ae. aegypti*, each confined in a lamp glass and provided with a mouse as source of blood (Pl. VIII, p. 121). Egg-maturation in this species takes about forty hours so that oviposition must be in some way staggered if there is to be a twenty-four-hour, rather than a forty-eight-hour rhythm in the population. It transpires that the effect is achieved by those individuals which become ready to oviposit after the end of a critical period each day, delaying their oviposition until the critical period on the following day. Thus, just as with the activity rhythm of *An. gambiae* (p. 111), the effect of the 'clock' is to prescribe the period during the twenty-four hours when activation is possible.

Resting

House resting is of special importance in relation to control with residual insecticides. We shall have more to say about it in the next chapter. Natural resting places are important from the point of view of epidemiological assessment since they may be expected to yield a less biassed sample of the mosquito population than do houses or animal shelters. They have, however, been much less extensively studied. In general it is more convenient to use artificial resting places such as pits, earth-lined boxes or stoneware jars (Fig. 31, p. 127). Even so, there is already ample evidence to show that nocturnal species are quite specific in their choice of daytime resting places. Studies on behaviour of this kind could well throw much light on the reactions of mosquitoes to their environment.

A prime requirement for a daytime resting place is that it should provide a tolerable microclimate. Many species show a preference for the darkest, most humid resting places available but this is not universally true (Pl. IX, p. 168). In a study of the resting habits of

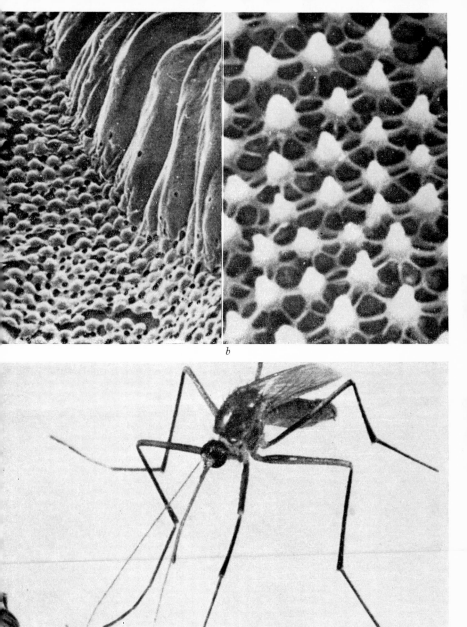

PLATE V Electron scan micrographs of mosquito eggs; mating in *Deinocerites*.
a. The plastron network, just below one of the floats, of *Anopheles stephensi* (x 900)
b. The plastron network of *Culex pipiens fatigans* (x 2250)   (*Photos: H. E. Hinton*)
c. Mating in *Deinocerites cancer*. In this species mating frequently takes place while the female is emerging from the pupa. The males seek out promising pupae, holding them by the trumpet with one pair of fore tarsal claws and sensing them with the greatly elongated antennae (from Provost and Haeger, *Ann. ent. Soc. Am.*, **60**: 571, 1967).

(*Photo: Joe O'Neal and J. S. Haeger*).

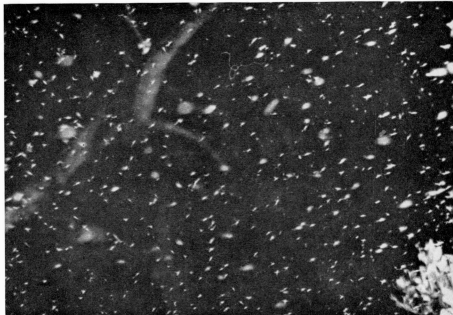

PLATE VI   Emergence and dispersal in *Aedes taenirohynchus*   *b*

a. Recent emergents resting on salt-marsh vegetation (Florida State Board of Health Entomology Research Center)   (*Photo: J. S. Haeger*).

b. A mass exodus from the breeding place. Departure begins during evening twilight when the mosquitoes are six hours or more old. It may be preceded by a meal of nectar, on the part of both sexes, if nectar is available. Mass mating may occur during the exodus (from Haeger, *Mosquito News,* **20**: 140, 1960   (*Photo: J. S. Haeger*).

PLATE VII

a. The high tower at Zika, Uganda. This tower, 120 ft. high was erected with funds supplied by WHO for the purpose of studying the behaviour of mosquitoes and other bloodsucking flies above, as well as in and below, the canopy. *(Photo: Information Department, East African Community).*

b. View of the canopy from the top of the tower. To the top left the forest grades through swamp forests and *Paspalum* swamp into an arm of Lake Victoria. To the right it passes abruptly into open grassland. Zika virus has been isolated on several occasions from mosquitoes flying above the canopy at a time when convection currents might be expected to disseminate them over considerable distances *(Photo: Author).*

Experimental set-up for studying the contribution of individual mosquitoes to the oviposition cycle. Each lamp-glass contains one male and one female mosquito. The mouse provides the blood-meal. Eggs are laid on the filter-paper cone which is kept moist by topping up the water in the beaker (from *A. Rep. E. Afr. Virus Res. Inst.*, **12**: 37, 1962).

mosquitoes in open grassland in South America collections were made with tent and cage traps, the grass inside being sprayed with an irritant (citronella) immediately after erection. These yielded mosquitoes in an average density of three million per sq. km. Males proved to be more numerous near breeding places but females occurred in more or less uniform density, with a slight tendency to concentration at intermediate distances (500-1,000 m.). Densities showed little tendency to diminish with distance from human settlements but blood-fed mosquitoes (particularly anophelines) were more numerous in proximity to these, suggesting that man provided a more abundant and accessible source of blood than the wild fauna. Flying mosquitoes were collected above the grass using sweep-nets attached to a moving vehicle (Pl. IX).

Hibernation

The potential importance of hibernating mosquitoes as winter

Fig. 29 Snow-covered rock scree in Washington State, a natural hibernation site of *Culex tarsalis*. Torpid mosquitoes are mostly found at a depth of 1½-3 ft but occasional individuals occur on the under-side of small frost-covered rocks at the surface. (After Rush et al., *Mosquito News*, **18**: 288, 1958)

refuges for arboviruses has already been noted (p. 65). In northerly parts of its range *Culex tarsalis* hibernates in great numbers in abandoned gold-mines and in rock screes (Fig. 29). Suspension of activity is complete and dormant females can be found flattened on the under side of small snow-covered stones or even resting on a thin film of frost. In contrast some *Anopheles* and *Culiseta* species undergo only a partial hibernation, becoming active with any amelioration of conditions. Partial hibernation of *An. labranchiae atroparvus* seems formerly to have been responsible, in part, for winter malaria in northern Europe (Ref. 3, p. 68). The subarctic *Culiseta impatiens* has been observed in active flight and resting on snow in January and February in Alaska.

The physiological mechanisms involved in hibernation are imperfectly understood. The subject has been well reviewed elsewhere.[10] Here we shall simply note that the onset of hibernation appears to be induced mainly by shortened photoperiod with an adjuvant effect of lowered temperature. Over-wintering females show a reduced tendency to take blood, in late autumn, coupled with hypertrophy of the fat-body and a failure of the eggs to mature in those individuals which do take blood (the so-called gonotrophic dissociation). Critical day lengths vary with latitude. Some subartic culicines appear not to take their first blood-meal until the second summer after emergence. Fig. 30 shows the sequence of springtime emergence, summer peak and autumn decline, dispersal and fat-body development in the population of a single resting site of *Culex tarsalis* in Colorado.

Aestivation

Despite its potential epidemiological importance the aestivation of tropical mosquitoes, during the dry season, has received comparatively little attention. There have been a number of reports suggestive of a prolongation of the time required to digest the blood-meal and a failure to develop eggs at this time, coupled with some experimental evidence for egg retention at low humidities and degeneration of unripe follicles in individuals with retained eggs. The very rapid appearance of species such as *An. gambiae* with the onset of the rains could well be explained by aestivation of gravid females. It seems that this is a field which might well repay exploration.

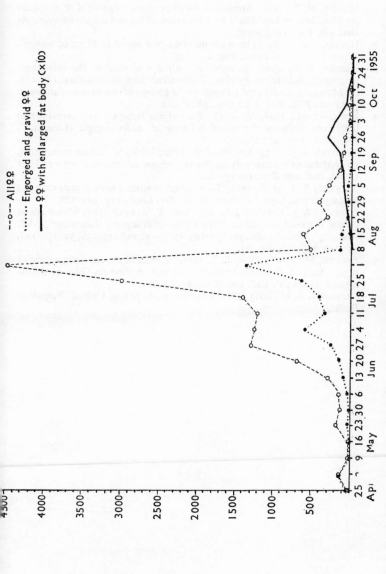

Fig. 30 Seasonal changes in the *Culex tarsalis* population in a resting site in Colorado. The numbers of hibernating and pre-hibernating females (with enlarged fat-body) are exaggerated by a factor of 10. (Based on Bennington et al., *Mosquito News*, **18**: 299, 1958).

Key:
- --o-- All ♀♀
- ...... Engorged and gravid ♀♀
- ——— ♀♀ with enlarged fat body (×10)

REFERENCES

1. GILLIES, M. T., 1961, 'Studies on the dispersion and survival of *Anopheles gambiae* Giles in East Africa by means of marking and release experiments *Bull. ent. Res.*, **52**: 99–127.
2. HOCKING, B., 1953, 'The intrinsic range and speed of flight of insects'. *Trans. R. ent. Soc. Lond.*, **104**: 223–345.
3. HAEGER, J. S., 1960, 'Behavior preceding migration in the salt-marsh mosquito', *Aedes taeniorhynchus* (Wiedemann). *Mosquito News*, **20**: 136–147.
4. DE MEILLON, B. et al., 1967, Papers on the biology of *Culex pipiens fatigans* in Rangoon. *Bull. Wld. Hlth Org.*, **36**: 1–180.
5. ROTH, L. M., 1948, 'A study of mosquito behavior. An experimental laboratory study of the sexual behavior of *Aedes aegypti* (Linnaeus)'. *Am. Midl. Nat.*, **40**: 265–352.
6. HADDOW, A. J., 1954, Studies of the biting habits of African mosquitoes, an appraisal of the methods employed, with special reference to the 24-hour catch'. *Bull. ent. Res.*, **45**: 199–242.
7. HADDOW, A. J., 1961, 'Entomological studies from a high tower in Mpanga forest, Uganda'. *Trans. R. ent. Soc. Lond.*, **113**: 249–368.
8. HADDOW, A. J., GILLETT, J. D. & CORBET, P. S., 1957–1961, 'Observations on the oviposition cycle of *Aedes* (*Stegomyia*) *aegypti* (Linnaeus)', I-VI. *Ann. trop. Med. Parasit.*, **51**: 159–169, **53**: 35–41 and 132–136, **54**: 156–164, **55**: 343–356 and 427–431.
9. GILLIES, M. T. & WILKES, T. J., 1965, 'A study of the age composition of populations of *Anopheles gambiae* Giles and A. *funestus* Giles in north-eastern Tanzania'. *Bull. ent. Res.*, **56**: 237–262.
10. CLEMENTS, A. N., 1963, *The Physiology of Mosquitoes*. Oxford: Pergamon Press.

VIII

The Biology of Control and Assessment

THE frequency and intensity of infection in the human population must always be the ultimate criteria of success in controlling mosquito-borne disease. By itself, however, the assessment of these parameters is seldom sufficient since it cannot explain the reasons for failure when this occurs. With all the improvements in drugs and vaccines which have taken place, extensive reliance still has to be placed on reduction of the vector. There is thus an ever-present need for improved methods of assessing the effect of control measures on the vector population. At the same time the interpretation of the results of such assessment calls for constant improvement in our understanding of vector behaviour. In this chapter we shall consider some of the factors affecting contact of the vector with man and his domestic environment, responses of the vector to insecticides and the assessment of vector potential and the effectiveness of measures designed to reduce it. Finally we shall discuss briefly some alternatives to house-spraying with residual insecticides which is still the principal weapon employed against anopheline (though not, in general, against culicine) vectors.

Host Choice

No species of mosquito feeds exclusively on man. Nor are vector species necessarily predominantly anthropophilic. It is possible that, except in special circumstances, only the highly domestic species *Aedes aegypti* and *C. p. fatigans* fall into this category. Some strains even of these species have been shown to be almost exclusively zoophilic. Savanna-dwelling anophelines seem, in general, to prefer ungulate hosts and may feed more extensively on domestic ungulates than on man even while serving as effective vectors. The banded-legged *Culex* transmitting various forms of encephalitis seem to owe their efficiency as vectors mainly to their unusual plasticity with regard to avian and mammalian hosts. *C. p. fatigans* for all its close association with man, feeds extensively on birds, including domestic poultry, even under urban conditions. *Ae. aegypti* shows marked plasticity, with reptiles appearing as the principal alternative host in one part of East Africa, rodents in another.

The use of the term 'host preference' in this connection is open to serious objection. Innate host preference is difficult to demonstrate except by sophisticated experimental techniques. Genetic differences certainly exist but there is no doubt that in many cases host availability plays a major, even a predominant, part. This in turn involves a variety of environmental factors in addition to mere predominance in numbers. For this reason we prefer to use the term 'host choice' in a purely objective sense as indicating the type of host which a particular kind of mosquito is observed most often to attack.

In a series of carefully designed experiments[1] a freshwater member and a brackish-water member of the *An. gambiae* complex were liberated together, first in a room containing a man and a calf and then in a corridor flanked by two compartments, containing man and calf respectively, with equal access to both. Both species fed preferentially on the calf but the difference was much more marked in the case of the brackish species (*An. merus*) as had been anticipated from epidemiological evidence and field observations. Very interestingly, the insertion of baffles permitting entry into the compartments but precluding exit from them, masked the difference between the two species, approximately 60 per cent of both feeding on man. It may be inferred from this that the approach to the host and the act of feeding need to be sharply distinguished. An animal which is more attractive at a distance may prove less so when actually encountered. For this there is also some evidence from the field. Another point which emerged clearly, as also from many field experiments, was the great variation in attractiveness as between individual hosts of the same species.

Field experiments on host attractivenesses are of two main kinds: those employing an unenclosed bait from which collections are made directly and those in which the bait is enclosed in a trap. Some of the very great variety of traps are illustrated in Fig. 31.

Many traps rely on an entrance in the form of a truncated cone or prism narrowing towards the interior on the principle of the lobster-pot. (On the same principle it is possible to imprison a number of mosquitoes in a test-tube by inserting into the open end a single

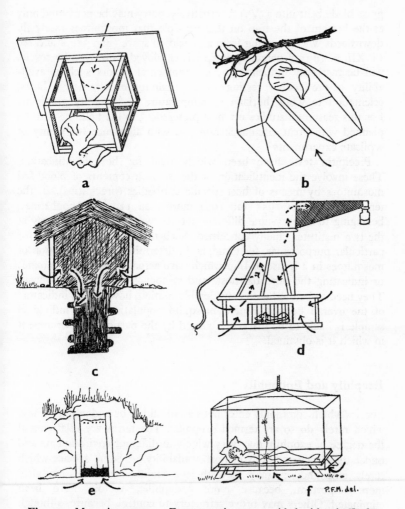

Fig. 31 Mosquito traps. **a** Entry or exit trap provided with a baffle for fixing over window-frame, **b** Muslin cage with entrance in the form of a truncated prism and space inside for two smaller cages containing bait. **c** Pit shelter shaded with thatch and with niches excavated in walls. **d** Baited suction trap with access to bait from all sides and also from above via slits between the transparent plates below fan-housing. **e** Wooden-framed cage with curtain inserted in earth bank. **f** Drop net, lowered while collecting mosquitoes resting inside. (**c** based on Gillies, *Bull. ent. Res.*, **45**: 361, 1954; **d** based on Lumsden, *Nature, Lond.*, **181**: 819, 1958).

grass-blade bent into a 'V'.) Alternatively, entry may be permitted only at the bottom of the trap on the principle that mosquitoes rarely fly downwards when escaping from an enclosed space (Fig. 31e, f and see Pl. XII, p. 169). Whatever principle is employed, however, the results will be markedly influenced by environmental factors such as availability of pre-feeding resting sites, proximity of alternative hosts, orientation to wind, horizon or temperature or humidity gradients. For this reason all studies on 'host preference', in the field, need to be planned with great circumspection and with allowance for plenty of replicate experiments.[2]

Precipitin tests have been widely used for host identification. These involve the identification of the stomach contents of blood-fed mosquitoes by means of host-specific antibodies (precipitins). In the ten years between 1955 and 1964 more than 120,000 Anophelines, belonging to seventy-nine different species, were tested in this way at the two institutes chiefly concerned. Such tests are of great value for particular purposes, as, for example, in determining the proportion of mosquitoes in a house or trap which have actually fed on the inmates or indicating the potential hosts and vectors involved in a zoonosis. They need to be used with considerable caution, however, as indicators of the overall behaviour of a mosquito population. Any individual sample is likely to be markedly biassed by the particular environment in which it is obtained.

Exophily and Endophily

Species which commonly enter houses are said to be endophilic. Those which rarely do so are termed exophilic. The terms are relative and the degree of exophily may vary widely in different environments and under different conditions of host availability.[3, 4] Some species which rarely enter houses may, nevertheless, maintain transmission after more important, because more endophilic, vectors have been eliminated. Others may prove refractory to control, because, although they enter houses to feed, they do not remain long enough, after feeding, to acquire a lethal dose of insecticide.

Among the various residual insecticides employed in house-spraying DDT is notably more irritant than the others. Irritancy appears to be independent of toxicity and to persist at a relatively high level after toxicity declines. The effect is sufficiently marked to lead to the escape of significant numbers of potential vectors from treated houses without these acquiring a lethal dose. This has to be offset against advantages such as low cost, relatively low toxicity to man and, particularly, less tendency to provoke insecticide resistance (see p. 148).

Insecticide avoidance of this kind has been thought to assume two different forms associated, respectively, with contact irritancy and long-distance repellency. The latter has been relatively little studied. Its existence cannot be said, as yet, to have been satisfactorily established. We shall therefore confine ourselves to contact repellency and the various behavioural components which this complex phenomenon involves. Genetical aspects of the matter will be dealt with in the next chapter. Many kinds of apparatus have been employed in the study of irritability (Fig. 32).[5]

In an early version (Fig. 32a) the mosquitoes were liberated in a central chamber with a removable, treated or untreated lining and with escape ports allowing access to either of two lateral chambers, one illuminated, the other darkened. In this way it was discovered that mosquitoes irritated by DDT show not only increased activity but also an increased positive phototaxy. This is important since it is likely to increase the chance of escape from a treated room whereas hyper-activity alone might merely lead to increased contact with the insecti-cide. It also suggests that the maintenance of uniform light conditions during irritability tests may be important. Subsequent experience has shown that this is certainly the case.

In a second type of apparatus (Fig. 32b) escape is permitted through cone- or prism-shaped ports or louvres which, at the same time, preclude re-entry into the treated release chamber. The extent of induced activity is assessed by counting the numbers of mosquitoes reaching successive escape chambers in a given interval of time. This apparatus has the advantage of obviating the need for continuous observation.

In a quite different category are those types of apparatus from which no escape is possible. In these the mosquitoes may be given a choice between a treated and an untreated surface. Alternatively they may be forced to rest on the treated surface, or remain in flight, by constructing the test chamber from a polished material (such as non-irritant plastic) which does not provide an acceptable resting surface. An example is shown in Fig. 32c. In this case the conical plastic exposure chamber is completely enclosed in a box so that light can gain entry only via the treated filter-paper. Before being introduced the mosquitoes are allowed a resting period during which they are 'conditioned' by exposure to untreated paper under similar illumination.

I

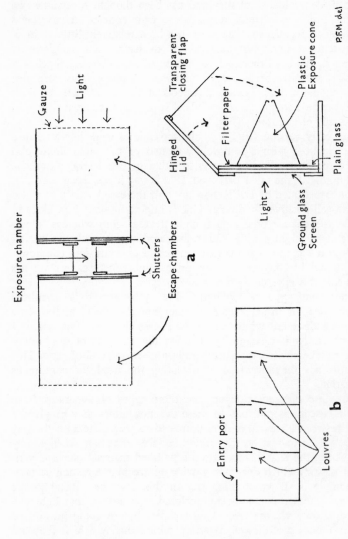

Fig. 32 Basic types of irritability test kit. For explanation see text. (**a** based on Kennedy, *Bull. ent. Res.*, **37**: 593, 1947; **b** based on Elliott, *Bull. Wld Hlth Org.*, **31**: 657, 1964; **c** based on Coluzzi, *Riv. Malariol.*, **42**: 189, 1963.)

In apparatus of this type irritability is measured first in terms of time to first take-off from the treated surface and secondly in terms of the number of take-offs during a standard interval of time. The two seem generally to be correlated but this cannot be assumed in individual cases. Neither alone can give an adequate measure of contact with the insecticide. For this it is necessary to know both the time spent initially at rest on the treated surface and the duration of successive flights (or the length of the intervals between them). Nor is increased flight activity necessarily the only manifestation of irritability. *Aedes aegypti* commonly shows increasing walking activity on treated surfaces. This could lead, in practice, to increased rather than diminished uptake of insecticide. Recently, a sound-recording apparatus resembling that described in connection with the recording of activity rhythms (p. 111) has been used for irritability studies. This allows testing in complete darkness and isolation from the observer, obviates the necessity for continuous monitoring and provides an automatic record of the precise time spent in contact with the insecticide. First results, still to be published, seem promising.

Other recent researches have employed tubular test-chambers of different lengths and with escape ports of different diameters. These have been used in genetic studies and will be discussed in the next chapter. Here we shall merely note that they have drawn attention to a third component of avoidance behaviour, in addition to enhanced activity and modified phototaxy. This is the ability or otherwise to negotiate an escape port. It is an aspect of behaviour still little understood but certainly of considerable importance in relation to entry into traps and into houses and worthy of further study from that point of view as well as for its intrinsic interest.

Insecticide Resistance

By resistance is meant the ability to withstand the toxic effects of an insecticide. Insecticide avoidance of the kind discussed in the previous section was at one time described as behavioural resistance, but this is merely confusing since resistance and avoidance are contradictory terms. The principal mode of defence against DDT (and, it would seem, against organo-phosphorus and carbamate compounds) is enzymic detoxication, the insecticide being destroyed before it can exert its full toxic effect. With the cyclical compounds dieldrin and benzene hexachloride the situation is different. Here there is little or no increased destruction of the insecticide. Resistant strains are characterized by little understood changes in tissue response. In both cases, however, the phenomenon is a genetical one. The appearance of resistance in previously susceptible populations is invariably the result of selection pressure exerted by the insecticide.

This is not to say that resistance necessarily results from anti-mosquito measures as such. On the contrary, there is good evidence that in a number of cases resistance has resulted indirectly from the use of agricultural insecticides (commonly employed on a much larger scale than those used for disease prevention). It seems probable that in such cases contamination of breeding places plays a major part, leading first to larval and then to adult resistance.

We shall deal more fully with the genetics of resistance in the next chapter. Here we shall discuss only some general features, illustrating these by reference to actual cases. Resistance to one or more of the four main groups of insecticides (DDT, cyclodiene compounds, organo-phosphorus compounds and carbamates) has been recorded in more than thirty species of *Anopheles,* including most of the major malaria vectors, and in some two dozen species of culicines. Dieldrin resistance, with cross-resistance to BHC, is the commonest but double resistance, to both DDT and dieldrin, has occurred in about twenty species (not always in the same population). No species has yet become resistant to any insecticide over the whole of its geographical range. Organo-phosphorus compounds have been used mainly as larvicides and chiefly against culicine mosquitoes. Some half-dozen species have become resistant to malathion either specifically or with cross-resistance to other O-P compounds such as parathion. Malathion resistance in *Aedes agegypti,* induced by laboratory selection, though itself of a low order was accompanied by strong cross-resistance to DDT and a significant cross-tolerance to one of the carbamates (Sevin).

DDT resistance tends to develop more slowly than dieldrin resistance. In some cases it has appeared too late to prevent the interruption of transmission (*An. culicifacies* in India, *An. aconitus* in part of Java). The effect may be enhanced by its irritancy which could by itself serve to reduce transmission, particularly when the vector is naturally exophilic and zoophilic. In consequence of this and of variations in its genetic dominance and of the level of resistance attained, the picture of DDT resistance within a single species can be quite complicated. Varying degrees of responsiveness of *An. stephensi* to DDT-spraying, in areas in which it became resistant (Fig. 33a) at

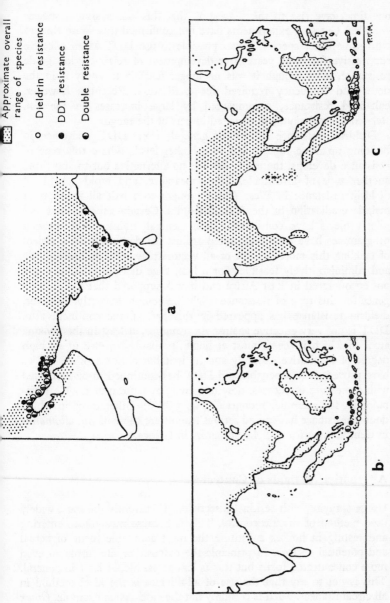

Fig. 33 Distribution of resistance in some species of *Anopheles* as of 1965. **a** *An. stephensi.* (A relict population was recently discovered on the Red Sea coast of Egypt but this is not shown). **b** *An. sundaicus.* **c** *An. aconitus.* (From various sources, notably Hamon & Garett-Jones, *Bull. Wld Hlth Org.*, **28**: 1, 1963 and Soerono et al., *ibid*, **32**: 161, 1965.)

Approximate overall range of species

○ Dieldrin resistance

● DDT resistance

◉ Double resistance

one time gave rise to the suggestion that this was a sibling species complex. Crossing experiments have not confirmed this. With this, as with some other species, it was possible to use DDT as an effective suppressive for some years after development of relatively low-grade resistance, even though it was no longer feasible to apply it in the doses and frequency required for eradication. Recently, however, enhanced resistance, accompanied by large increases in the *An. stephensi* population, has occurred in part of the range.

Dieldrin resistance differs, in general, from DDT resistance in building up more rapidly and to a higher level. Where this type of resistance develops, therefore, there is no alternative but to substitute another type of insecticide. The appearance, and rapid spread, of dieldrin resistance in West Africa brought to a halt all attempts at malaria eradication in the African tropics. Certain experimental and pilot projects have continued but, in general, training and research programmes have been substituted against the day when the problem of tackling this most difficult of all vectors may seem technologically and administratively feasible. For a long time dieldrin resistance was not encountered in East Africa and it was supposed that the gene or genes for this type of resistance might be absent. Recently, however, dieldrin resistance has appeared in this part of the continent also. DDT is not very effective against *An. gambiae,* at least in the savanna areas in which it seems most at home, probably because of its high degree of facultative exophily and its irritability. Some other species have proved more amenable and DDT has continued to be employed with a measure of success, despite a complex pattern of double resistance in, for example, Indonesia (Fig. 33b, c). Other cases in which double resistance has caused serious trouble are those of *An. albimanus* in Central America and *An. sacharovi* in Greece.

Alternative Methods of Control

House-spraying with residual insecticides is currently the most widely used method of disease control. This is because mosquitoes entering and resting in houses constitute the most accessible focus of actual and potential vectors. In principle the oviposition site forms an even more concentrated focus but this is less accessible, at least in general. This is not to say that the use of adulticides is the ideal method in all circumstances. Such is certainly not the case. As an example, *Culex pipiens fatigans,* combining, as it does, a particular proneness to develop resistance to DDT and the dieldrin groups of insecticides with relatively accessible urban breeding places, is likely to continue to be dealt with mainly by anti-larval measures (or genetical control). Many other special cases could be quoted. When there are added to these the great variety of cases in which house-spraying, though effective, is not totally so and requires to be reinforced by additional measures, it will be seen that the need for alternative methods of control is already very great. It may well become greater as the development of insecticide resistance proceeds. It is likely that, in the last analysis, the most economic control programmes will be those employing a variety of weapons in the most efficient combination possible.

By far the most satisfactory, because most permanent, method of larval control is the large scale modification of breeding grounds by drainage, flushing, admission of salt-water, earth filling or other engineering methods. Such undertakings are costly but can be made profitable, particularly if they result in the reclamation of waste land. Just as the capital expenditure involved is large so also are the economies which may be made by elucidating the precise breeding requirements of the vector species. A good example is the discovery of the specific association of *Anopheles melas* with *Avicennia* (as opposed to *Rhizophora*) mangrove which made it possible to concentrate attention on 'orchards' of the former among large areas of the latter (see Ref. 4, p. 101). Another method falling under the general heading of environmental sanitation is the regular emptying of containers, potential breeding places for *Aedes aegypti*, which need, in principle, involve no more than legislation and adequate enforcement. This method alone proved adequate, in the past, for the elimination of urban yellow fever from major centres of human population in the tropics and is currently playing a major part in the campaign for the eradication of *Aedes aegypti* from the New World (p. 66). Adequate provision for the disposal of domestic and industrial waste could suffice to eliminate urban filariasis transmitted by *Culex pipiens fatigans*. Brugian filariasis has been successfully controlled in certain areas by the destruction, with herbicides, of vegetation harbouring early stages of *Mansonia* species as an adjunct to chemotherapy.

'Biological control' is generally taken to mean the use, for purposes of vector reduction, of living agents, parasites or predators. Predators on the eggs, larvae and pupae, or adults of mosquitoes are found among all the classes of vertebrates and among six phyla of invertebrates, the Coelenterata, Rotatoria, Platyhelminthes, Annelida, Mollusca and Arthropoda. The list of those employed with any degree of success for the control is much shorter including as it does only fish and the predatory larvae of *Toxorhynchites*, while even the latter appear to have only a very restricted usefulness (p. 76). Fish, on the other hand have probably been more widely and successfully employed than is commonly realized. The mosquito fish, *Gambusia affinis* has been introduced from the southern United States throughout the warmer parts of the world and now, probably, has the widest geographical range of any freshwater fish. Cold-hardy strains have become established as far north as Canada and the USSR. Other widely used species include tooth-carp (*Panchax* spp.) and guppies (*Lebistes reticulatus*), the latter particularly valuable by reason of its tolerance of heavy organic pollution. Particular interest is currently being shown in annual fishes with eggs requiring a period of desiccation, followed by flooding, before they will hatch.

Parasites of mosquitoes are even more varied and numerous. They include viruses, resembling the *Tipula* iridescent virus, rickettsiae and spirochaets (neither very strongly pathogenic), bacteria, fungi (especially *Coelomomyces* spp., for which see below), many Protozoa, rotifers, nematodes (especially Mermithidae), trematodes and mites. Very few of these have been at all adequately studied. Among the more promising would seem to be some microsporidian Protozoa, possibly to be the subject of a field trial in the near future, mermithid nematodes, successfully cultured in the laboratory and also due to be tested in the field and, particularly, *Coelomomyces*, the only group, as yet, to be successfully employed in a field trial. One of the forty or so currently recognized species, *C. stegomyiae*, was introduced from Singapore into Nukunono Atoll, in the central Pacific, in 1958, to study the effects on the local filariasis vector, *Aedes polynesiensis*. Five years later parasitized larvae were recovered from 37 per cent of the breeding places sampled. Another species has been observed to cause heavy mortality among *Anopheles gambiae* larvae in the field. This species is being actively studied. At the same time new parasites are constantly being sought. The World Health Organization has recently made available a collecting kit for the storage and transport of infected arthropod vectors and has established an international reference centre for the provision of identifications and material for research.

Epidemiologcal Assessment

With the advent of computers the chief aim of the epidemiologist, the understanding and prediction of the forms assumed by communicable disease, seems to have taken a long step nearer realization. No computer programme, or other mathematical model, can, however, operate in a vacuum. The cogency and validity of the results that it yields must always depend on the cogency and validity of the data fed to it (or employed for checking its predictions). Some of the factors determining the shape of an arthropod-borne disease were outlined in Chapter 1. We shall take this as read and confine ourselves, as an example, to a single parameter and the means by which it is assessed, choosing for the purpose the life-expectancy of the vector. As we already saw, this is a crucial factor. The pathogen can only become infective to the host if the vector lives long enough. Thereafter transmission can only be maintained if the vector survives long enough to transmit the pathogen to sufficient hosts and, indirectly, sufficient other vectors for the infection to reproduce itself. If the reproduction rate falls, and is maintained, below 1, the disease will die out. This is the kernel of eradication.

A rough estimate of life-expectancy could, in principle, be arrived at by the release and recapture of marked mosquitoes of known age. Except in very special circumstances, however, such an estimate would be unlikely to be sufficiently accurate to be of use. The much more accurate methods currently employed are based on estimates of the proportion of the population surviving through natural episodes of known duration. As an example, the ratio (parous)/(parous + nulli-parous) females can be used as an estimate of the proportion surviving through a single gonotrophic cycle. If 'p' is the daily survival rate then 'p^n' may be expected to survive at the end of a gonotrophic cycle lasting 'n' days. Conversely the nth root of the proportion parous gives a measure of the daily survival rate.

Another, comparable, method employs infected mosquitoes. In this case the calculation is based on the known duration of stages in the development of the parasite, e.g. the interval between the development of oocysts and the appearance of sporozoites in the salivary glands, in the case of malaria, or the intervals between various developmental stages of filarial larvae. Both these approaches have yielded useful results, the first being generally preferred by reason of the much greater numbers of parous than of infective females. Neither method, however, gives any direct measure of the age of individual mosquitoes. Concealed variables may thus invalidate the analysis.

This disadvantage has been overcome by a technique developed in the Soviet Union during the years immediately following the Second

World War. The method, in this case, involves the direct recording of the number of ovarian cycles undergone by the individual female. This is rendered possible by the fact that each successive egg develops at a point anterior to the preceding one and leaves behind it a perceptible dilatation after passing down the ovariolar 'stalk' on its way to the oviduct (see Plate X). A count of the maximum number of dilations observable on the individual ovariolar 'stalks' thus provides a direct record of the number of ovarian cycles experienced by the particular individual. The technique is difficult but rewarding and, in skilled hands, can yield a remarkable variety of useful and reliable information.[6]

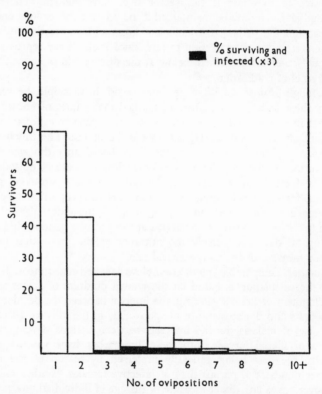

Fig. 34 Percentage of *Anopheles gambiae* surviving through successive gonotrophic cycles. The shaded area shows the percentage surviving *and* infected exaggerated by a factor of three. (Based on Gillies & Wilkes, *Bull. ent. Res.*, **56**: 237, 1965 and Gillies, *Penguin Science Survey*, **B** 163, 1966.)

Fig. 34 shows dramatically how small a proportion even of such a dangerous and long-lived vector as *An. gambiae* actually become infected and survive thereafter long enough to transmit the disease. In spite of this it has been found that in parts of Africa volunteers sleeping in experimental huts may each receive more than 200 bites from infected mosquitoes in the course of a year.

As an alternative to full-scale age-grading much useful information can be gained from a simple analysis of the female population into parous and nulliparous. This rests on the fact that, in nulliparous females, the finer tracheoles are tightly coiled whereas, in those which have deposited one or more egg batches, they uncoil and unravel, giving a highly characteristic appearance. The technique needs to be employed with caution when examining resting females since uncoiling begins at an early stage in egg-maturation and may be exhibited in an advanced degree by nulliparous females after taking the first blood-meal. As applied to females coming to feed, however, it has given excellent results and yielded, in particular, useful information regarding changes in the structure of mosquito populations in response to natural or artificial changes in the environment (Ref. 4, p. 124).

REFERENCES

1. GILLIES, M. T., 1967, Experiments on host selection in the *Anopheles gambiae* complex. *Ann. trop. Med. Parasit.*, **61**: 68–75.
2. REID, J. A., 1961, The attraction of mosquitoes by human or animal baits in relation to the transmission of disease. *Bull. ent. Res.*, **52**: 43–62.
3. GILLIES, M. T., 1956, The problem of exophily in *Anopheles gambiae*. *Bull. Wld Hlth Org.*, **15**: 437–449.
4. MATTINGLY, P. F., 1962, Mosquito behaviour in relation to disease eradication programmes. *A. Rev. Ent.*, **7**: 419–436.
5. BUSVINE, J. R., 1964, The significance of DDT-irritability tests on mosquitoes. *Bull. Wld Hlth Org.*, **31**: 645–656.
6. DETINOVA, T. S., 1968, Age structure of insect populations of medical importance. *A. Rev. Ent.*, **13**: 427–450.

IX

Mosquito Genetics

MOSQUITOES make excellent genetical material, offering, among other advantages, rapid development, ease of rearing in large numbers, the possession by aedine genera of resistant eggs obviating the necessity for the maintenance of permanent colonies and, in some species at least, a high natural mutation rate. The difficulty of mating eurygamous species has been overcome by the development of artificial mating techniques involving the decapitation of the male and the application of his terminalia to those of the anaesthetized female (see Pl. XI). The literature, though mostly recent, is extensive, but it has been well summarized.[1, 2, 3, 4]

Cytology and Cytogenetics

All those mosquitoes so far studied (about seventy species belonging to twelve different genera) have a haploid chromosome number of three. This may have been derived from the number four, commoner in Diptera generally, by fusion of the sex chromosome with one of the autosomes. Small supernumary bodies have been observed during prophase in some *Toxorhynchites, Orthopodomyia, Aedes* and *Anopheles* but it is not clear that these represent anything other than detached fragments of autosomes. Early accounts of chromosome numbers other than three are attributable to the unusually close pairing of homologous chromosomes during early mitosis, characteristic also of many other Diptera.

In culicine mosquitoes all three pairs of chromosomes are closely similar except in size (Fig. 35d-f). Sex chromosomes have not been identified. In anophelines, on the other hand, sex chromosomes can be recognized and these commonly vary markedly as between species (Fig. 35a, b). The X chromosomes show extensive banding in salivary gland preparations and are very useful for the identification of other-

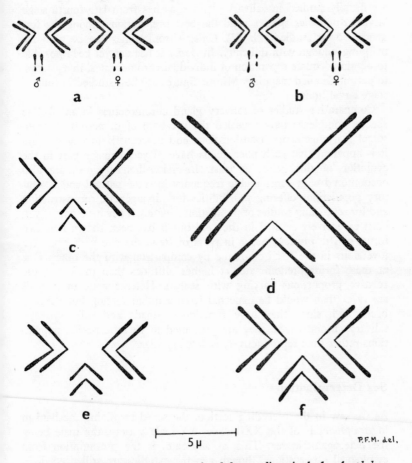

├────── 5 μ ──────┤

P.F.M. del.

Fig. 35 Mosquito karyotypes. **a** *Anopheles maculipennis* s.l. **b** *Anopheles quadrimaculatus*. **c** *Wyeomyia smithii*. **d** *Aedes stimulans*. **e** *Aedes togoi*. **f** *Culex pipiens*. (**a** after Kitzmiller (ref. 1 p. 155); remainder after Rai, *Ann. ent. Soc. Am.*, **56**: 160, 1963.)

wise similar members of difficult species complexes (Fig. 42, p. 161 and see Pl. XI).

Giant chromosomes are found not only in the larval salivary glands but also in the malpighian tubules and parts of the gut though they are usually studied in salivary gland squashes from late fourth-stage larvae. *Anopheles* species yield the best preparations among the few genera so far studied (Pl. XI). *Culex* chromosomes can be used for mapping, though with difficulty. In *Aedes* it has not yet been possible to obtain adequate separation of individual chromosomes, in squashes, to permit detailed mapping. Mitotic figures are best studied in fourth-stage larval brain.

Comparative studies of salivary gland chromosomes in anopheline species complexes have revealed the presence of numerous chromosomal rearrangements (translocations and paracentric inversions) and it is apparent that such phenomena have played a major part in the evolution of this genus at least. Inversion heterozygotes are also encountered with considerable frequency in some natural and laboratory populations offering possibilities for phylogenetic reconstruction and for rewarding studies of population genetics. They have not, as yet, been extensively studied in the field but it has been shown that two forms of *An. messeae* occur in parts of Italy, the one with extensive inversions in the X-chromosome by comparison with the other. One of these forms predominates at higher altitudes than the other, the relative proportions varying with season. Heterozygous individuals are rarer than would be expected from random mating but they do occur and, since they have functional gonads and fully synaptic salivary chromosomes, they are presumed to be intraspecific populations rather than reproductively isolated species.

Sex Determination

As we saw in the preceding section, the sex-determining mechanism in *Anopheles* is of the XX-female, XY-male variety, the male being the heterogametic sex. This, at any rate, is the presumption from cytological observations, though genetical studies are still needed. In culicines the situation is a little better. In *Aedes aegypti* some eighty mutant genes have been identified, more than twenty of them located in linkage groups. Cross-over studies, using marker genes, have shown that in this species and *Culex pipiens* sex is determined by a single gene or small group of genes in a non-terminal position (throwing some doubt on the derivation of the reduced chromosome number by

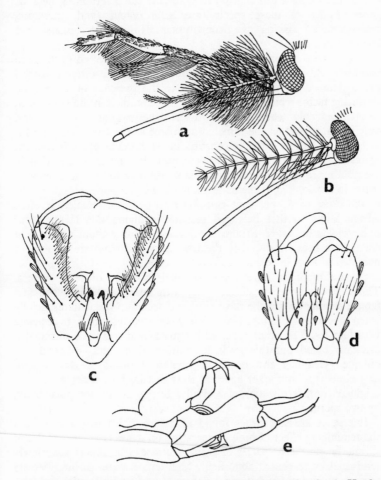

Fig. 36 *Aedes (Ochlerotatus) stimulans.* **a** Head of normal male. **b** Head of male feminized by rearing at 28·4°C. **c** Terminalia of normal male, **d** Terminalia of partly feminized male reared at 27°C. **e** Male with two sets of terminalia, reared initially at 28·4°C and during 4th instar at 18°C. (Redrawn, in part, from Anderson & Horsfall, *J. exp. Zool.*,**154**: 67, 1963 and Horsfall & Anderson, *Science, N.Y.*, **141**: 1183, 1963.)

fusion between sex chromosome and autosome, suggested above, since this would imply a terminal position for the sex determining gene or genes. Males of these species are heterozygous (and, therefore, heterogametic) having the constitution Mm, while females are homozygous, mm.

Under these circumstances the sexes might be expected to occur in roughly equal numbers. In practice, however, there is often a marked preponderance of males. This is due to the presence of a sex-ratio distorting factor which has been isolated and studied in the laboratory. It operates only when present in the heterozygous condition and only when located on the same chromosome as the dominant gene for male, i.e. in fathers with the constitution $M^D m^d$. The effect is thought to result from disturbances during meiosis leading to a reduction in the number of female-producing sperm and thus to resemble 'meiotic drive' in *Drosophila*. It seems that a moderate preponderance of males, or the order of 60 per cent as against 40 per cent females, is often advantageous so that balanced systems involving this factor occur quite widely in nature. Strains consistently yielding about 90 per cent males have been produced in the laboratory and these are of obvious potential interest in relation to genetical control.

Gynandromorphs have been recorded in many different genera. Those of the antero-posterior type, with bushy male antennae and female terminalia, are the most readily detected in the field, especially when they attempt to take blood. They also try, sometimes, to copulate with females. The other type, with female head and male terminalia, can take blood but this leads to rupture of the gut. Bilateral and oblique gynanders also occur in laboratory stocks of *Ae. aegypti*. Experiments with marker genes suggest that in this species gynanders originate from fertilization of a binulceate egg, or egg and polar body, by two sperm.

Intersexes are sometimes found in nature which may result from the feminizing effect of high temperature on males (Fig. 36). Males of several far-northern species of *Ochlerotatus* can be almost completely feminized by rearing at abnormally high temperature. At intermediate temperatures, intermediates are produced and under special temperature regimes a second set of crudely formed male terminalia may develop from the eighth abdominal segment.

Two intersex-producing strains of *Ae. aegypti*, having different temperature thresholds, have been studied. In the one with the higher threshold, temperatures of 35-37°C were required for full morphological feminization. In this case the effect is under the control of a single autosomal recessive sex-limited gene. Feminized males take blood and can produce fully mature eggs but have so far failed to oviposit. Feminized males of *Ochlerotatus* cannot be persuaded to take blood but their ovaries will mature if transplanted into normal blood-fed females. Genetically male primordia develop into ovaries, at the appropriate temperature, even when transplanted into species remaining morphologically male at that temperature. An intersex-producing gene, apparently temperature independent, has been recorded in *Culex pipiens*.

Experimental Taxonomy

Modifying effects of the environment on characters used in mosquito taxonomy have been too little studied to permit of any extensive generalizations. Such as they are, however, such studies suggest that environmental effects of this kind are unlikely to deceive a competent taxonomist who pays adequate attention to characters other than purely morphological ones (see, e.g. Refs. 1 and 5, p. 167). More rewarding have been studies designed to ascertain whether small morphological differences, coupled, in some cases, with important biological ones, are truly indicative of species status, i.e. of reproductive isolation between their possessors. Generally speaking the answer has been that good species show much smaller differences than an earlier generation of taxonomists would have suspected. Cases of this kind will form the subject of the next chapter.

In contrast to this are the marked variations in male terminalia, under genetic control, in the single species *Culex pipiens* and a wide range of variation in colour characters within the species *Ae. aegypti* involving both major genes and multiple alleles. Particular interest attaches to colour variation in this species since it has been shown to be directly associated with behavioural differences.

Experimental approaches to mosquito taxonomy have included interspecific hybridization, comparative serology and chromatography and numerical taxonomy, used as an experimental method of the comparison of phenetic with phyletic or larval with adult classifications. These approaches have been recently reviewed.[4] We shall confine ourselves to a single example of some of the very interesting problems which arise.

Various reports of successful hybridization between *Ae. aegypti* and *Ae. albopictus* are now thought to have resulted from contamination of breeding stocks. In all these cases the supposed hybrid offspring was morphologically identical with one or other parent. A formidable

K

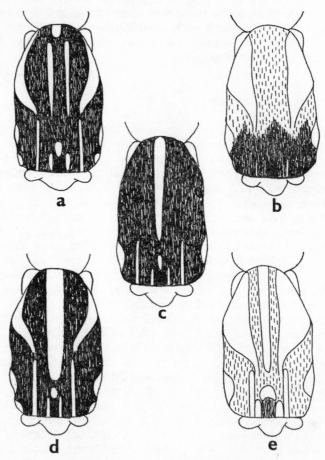

Fig. 37 Mesonotal ornamentation in subgenus *Stegomyia*. **a** *Ae. aegypti*, type form. **b** *Ae. mascarensis*. **c** *Ae. albopictus*. **d** *Ae. aegypti-albopictus* hybrid. **e** *Ae. vinsoni*. Diagrammatic, especially **d** and **e** which are based on unique, imperfect specimens.

series of mutually reinforcing barriers to hybridization has been demonstrated. Nevertheless one undoubted laboratory hybrid, morphologically intermediate between the parents, has been obtained (Fig. 37a, c, d). *Ae. aegypti* has been eradicated from the island of Mauritius but there remains there a fully reproductively compatible wild species (or subspecies) *Ae. mascarensis* (Fig. 37b). Two wild-caught mosquitoes from the same island, provisionally named as a distinct species, *Ae. vinsoni*, are intermediate in a number of respects between *Ae. mascarensis* and *Ae. albopictus*, one in particular, quite strongly recalling the successful *aegypti-albopictus* hybrid (Fig. 37e). In its mesonotal ornamentation, though not in other characters, *Ae. mascarensis* shows a strong resemblance to certain members of the very distinct *Ae. (Finlaya) niveus* group, which might be thought to suggest that it is in some respects more primitive, or at least atavistic, than *Ae. aegypti* s.str. It is also, if possible, even more variable with respect to its colour characters than the latter. Having regard to these facts some small doubt may be felt as to whether the barriers to hybridization between *Ae. albopictus* and *Ae. mascarensis* would prove altogether as formidable as those between *Ae. albopictus* and *Ae. aegypti* s.str. The frequent occurrence in mosquitoes of striking resemblances in ornamentation between individual species belonging to quite different genera and subgenera suggests the existence of epigenetic phenomena of very considerable interest.

Genetics of Vectorial Capacity

Variations in infectibility as between different strains of vector, and as between individuals of the same strain, are a familiar feature of studies on laboratory transmission. In some cases, at least, the genetic basis of such variation is comparatively simple. Susceptibility of *Ae. aegypti* to infection with subperiodic *Brugia malayi* is controlled by a single recessive sex-linked gene with, as might be expected, some modification by genetic background. Preliminary experiments suggest that susceptibility of *Ae. aegypti* to *Plasmodium gallinaceum* and, possibly, of *C. pipiens* to *P. cathemaerium* are also under the control of a single gene or group of closely linked genes.

Interestingly, *Ae. aegypti* selected for susceptibility to subperiodic also becomes susceptible to periodic *B. malayi* and to *B. pahangi* and both periodic and subperiodic *Wuchereria bancrofti*. As we saw (p. 46) these all develop in the thoracic muscles of the mosquito.

Susceptibility to *Dirofilaria immitis,* which develops in the malpighian tubules, is under separate genetic control.

Attempts have been made to assess the deleterious effect of *B. malayi* on the vector by feeding susceptible and non-susceptible strains of *Ae. aegypti* on infected cats. Differential mortality might be expected to lead to a progressive reduction in the proportion of susceptibles through successive generations. In the event, however, no such difference was observed, possibly because cage populations are subject to too little stress for an effect to be apparent.

Differences in vector susceptibility as observed in nature are not, of course, necessarily a reflection of differences in the vectors. They are due in many cases to differences between particular strains of pathogens. As an example, the same urban strain of *C. p. fatigans,* in Malaya, has been found to be highly susceptible to urban, and comparatively refractory to rural, *W. bancrofti.* Very little work has been done on the genetics of mosquito-borne pathogens but it was recently shown, in a marathon experiment, that the infection rate of *Aedes togoi* with *Brugia patei,* having a microfilarial generation time of about one year, progressively increased from 43.6 per cent to 89.8 per cent during selection through four generations.

Genetics of Insecticide Resistance

The study of resistance genetics of mosquitoes has a history of little more than 10 years. Progress has been considerable but, despite the importance of the subject, much has still to be learned. Early work on *Anopheles* showed dieldrin resistance to be partly dominant with clear-cut segregation, so that proportions of homozygous resistants and susceptibles and of heterozygotes could be readily estimated by the use of discriminating doses of insecticide (Fig. 38).

More recently fully dominant dieldrin resistance has appeared in some populations of *An. gambiae,* possibly under separate genetic control, though this requires confirmation. Studies of this kind in *Anopheles,* are hampered by lack of marker genes. This situation is being remedied. Dieldrin resistance is also monofactorial in both *Ae. aegypti* and *C. p. fatigans* and the gene concerned has been located, in both cases, in its linkage group. In *Ae. aegypti* the genes for dieldrin and DDT resistance are located close together on the same chromosome so that there is a tendency for the same insecticide to select for both types of resistance.

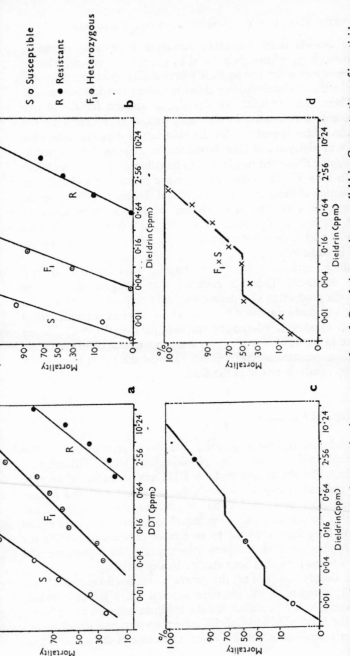

Fig. 38 Resistance genotypes. **a** *Ae. aegypti* resistant to DDT. **b, c, d** *C. p. fatigans* resistant to dieldrin. Concentrations of insecticide are plotted along the abscissa on a logarithmic scale. Percentage mortalities are plotted along the ordinate on a probit scale which has the effect of straightening out the sinusoidal response curve. In the case of DDT resistance the regression lines generally overlap to an extent which renders impossible the use of simple discriminating doses. It will be seen from **b**, however, that 0.02 ppm of dieldrin kills all susceptibles, while leaving heterozygotes and homozygous resistants untouched. At the same time 0.32 ppm kills all but resistants. **c** shows a hypothetical population of the same strain comprising 25% susceptible, 50% heterozygous and 25% resistant with conspicuous 'steps' at the 25% and 75% level. **d** shows an actual population resulting from a back-cross of F_1 heterozygotes to susceptibles with the 'step' this time at the 50% level. (**a** based on Klassen & Brown, *Canad. J. Genet. Cytol.*, **6**:61, 1964; **b–d** based on Tadano & Brown, *Bull. Wld. Hlth Org.*, **36**:101, 1967.)

Unlike dieldrin resistance, DDT resistance is generally recessive. It is also much more strongly affected by genetic background. Homozygous recessives differ less in their susceptibility from heterozygotes so that the use of discriminatory doses is subject to wider margins of error. These characteristics are thought to account for the slower development of resistance, in the field, in face of selection by the insecticide. There is evidence for the existence of different factors for resistance in Malayan and New World strains of *aegypti*, but chromosome mapping shows the two factors to be either allelic or very closely linked. In New World strains the resistance factor is associated with the production of the detoxifying enzyme DDT-dehydrochlorinase and this seems to constitute the principal resistance mechanism. In Malayan strains, on the other hand, although dehydrochlorination plays some part it does not seem to be the only, or even the major, element in resistance.

Malathion resistance in *Culex tarsalis* is monofactorial and partially dominant. There is evidence that the gene in question controls the production of a detoxifying enzyme (carboxyesterase). In contrast, low-grade resistance in larvae of *Ae. aegypti* is multifactorial and is associated with reduced absorption of the insecticide. Carbamate resistance in larvae of *C. p. fatigans* and cross-resistance to carbamate in malathion resistant *aegypti* are multifactorial and might be expected to develop relatively slowly in the field.

Physiological Genetics

Most work on resistance genetics has been carried out at the biochemical rather than the physiological level. Physiological mechanisms thought to contribute to DDT resistance in *Ae. aegypti*, such as reduced absorption through the larval gut wall and integument and increased production of peritrophic membrane, are apparently polygenic. Other genetical studies of physiological characters have been confined to aspects or reproduction. Only the mode of inheritance of autogeny (the capacity for egg-maturation without a blood-meal) has been studied in any detail.

As we already saw (p. 114) the genera *Toxorhynchites* and *Malaya* are wholly autogenous. Certain other species, e.g. *Wyeomyia smithii*, may be exclusively autogenous, but the evidence is far from conclusive. Among the Anophelini and Culicini more than forty species are known to be partly autogenous but in no case is this true of the entire species population. Only one of these species, *Culex pipiens*, has been the subject of detailed genetic analysis.

In *C. p.* var. *molestus* (p. 164) autogeny is apparently under the control of two distinct major genes situated on different chromosomes, one sex-linked, the other represented by multiple alleles. *C. pipiens* s.str. undergo winter diapause with hypertrophy of the fat-body. *C. p.* var. *molestus* cannot do this and rely instead on a combination of underground breeding and autogeny in the northern part of their range. Preliminary studies suggest that these differences have a quite simple genetic basis. Hybrids can be recognized by the segregation of autogeny and anautogeny in their progeny but further study of the population genetics of this character must await a more detailed analysis of its mode of inheritance.

So far as is known at present, autogeny, except in *Toxorhynchites* and *Malaya*, is essentially a characteristic of non-tropical mosquitoes. It has been recorded once or twice in *Aedes aegypti*, maintained by normal laboratory methods, but these records require confirmation. Certainly it is at best extremely rare in this species. Nevertheless the genetic potential is present, a fact of considerable interest in relation to the supposed primitiveness or otherwise of the bloodsucking habit. Selection through successive generations fed on egg albumin and sucrose has resulted in the appearance, in the F_8, of females capable of producing viable eggs on sucrose alone. Small numbers of autogenous females have also been found in a laboratory colony maintained over a period of years on sucrose and citrated beef blood. The genetic and endocrinal bases of egg-maturation seem to be of comparable complexity. A one-gene – one-hormone relationship is perhaps too much to hope for but further exploration on these lines might well be rewarding.

Behaviour Genetics

The boundary between behaviour genetics and physiological genetics is sometimes arbitrary. As an example, strains of *Aedes aegypti* differ in the ability of virgin females to lay eggs when given a blood-meal. The difference is now known to be one of response to the stimulatory effect of male accessory gland secretion on ovulation. There is no evidence of any difference in oviposition behaviour subsequent to the release of the ripe oocyte into the oviduct. The mode of inheritance of this character has not been fully studied but preliminary studies suggest that it may be under the control of a single dominant gene permitting ovulation by virgin females. It seems more appropriate to treat this, in future, under the heading of physiological, rather than behaviour, genetics.

More strictly behavioural characters might be found in the minutiae of oviposition behaviour affecting, for example, the shape of the *Culex* egg raft or the choice of oviposition surfaces. Different strains of *aegypti* differ markedly in the extent to which they will lay their eggs on open water instead of above the water-line. Crossing experiments, between strains selected for this character, are compatible with control by a single sex-linked gene for dry laying with incomplete dominance. Other characters, with more obvious adaptive significance, shown to respond to selection, include 'preferences' for dark or illuminated oviposition sites, spreading of oviposition over shorter or longer periods following the blood-meal and responses of the pre-larvae to hatching stimuli.

The genetics of mating behaviour have been widely studied in *Drosophila*, much less so in mosquitoes. Stenogamy (p. 105) appears in the F_1 from crosses between members of the *Culex pipiens* and *Anopheles maculipennis* complexes, and in the offspring from back-crosses where the F_1 males are sterile. Many species adapt rapidly to cage conditions, once established, but the behavioural and genetic bases of this character have been very inadequately studied. The same applies to differences in mating vigour and epigamic behaviour in the *An. maculipennis*, *C. pipiens* and *Aedes scutellaris* complexes. How-ever, the gene for yellow larva has been shown to confer enhanced mating vigour on males of *Ae. aegypti*, contributing to the establish-ment of a balanced polymorphism in laboratory colonies with 70-75 per cent yellow individuals. Females seem to show little discrimina-tion with regard to mates and some degree of multiple insemination has to be allowed for in this species, though not, apparently in *C. pipiens*.

Mosquitoes, once established in cage colonies, also tend to adapt rapidly to new hosts. Some particularly striking examples have been recorded in *C. p. fatigans* but their genetic basis has not been explored. Reference has already been made to the necessity for rigorous control of experimental conditions in this type of study as illustrated by work on host choice in *An. gambiae* (p. 126). This is another field in which behaviour and physiology merge imperceptibly and much diversity is to be expected at every level. Adenosine-5'-phosphate has been shown to act as a powerful phagostimulant in *C. pipiens*, ATP in *Ae. aegypti*, while it is claimed that adenine nucleotides are with-out effect on engorgement in *Culiseta inornata*. Different species also vary widely in their response to different types of blood. *C. pipiens* produces much larger rafts when fed on bird blood than when fed on mammal blood. In contrast *Ae. aegypti* has been found to produce more eggs per mg. of ingested blood when fed on rabbit or guinea pig than when fed on canary or turtle.

The host choice experiments with *An. gambiae* were followed by selection through a small number of generations for anthropophily and zoophily. Both types of behaviour showed marked enhancement but relaxation of selection pressure was followed by rapid reversion to the original pattern. In *An. labranchiae atroparvus* selection through thirty-two generations was required to establish stabilized strains differing in flight activity and escape behaviour following contact with DDT (p. 129).

Genetic Control

Genetic control implies the deliberate manipulation of the hereditary material available to the vector population. The accent is on the word deliberate since any form of interference with natural populations necessarily involves genetic consequences (as shown, for example, by the emergence of insecticide resistance). Methods currently envisaged mostly involve a simple reduction in the available genetic material by sterilization of one or both sexes, usually only the male. More positive approaches, by the deliberate spreading of deleterious factors, pose many difficulties though it has been suggested that some of these might be reduced by exploiting meiotic drive (p. 144) or, e.g., the combination of deleterious with resistance genes and their joint introduction into non-resistant populations.

Methods available for the production of sterile males already go well beyond the use of gamma-radiation, from a cobalt source, employed unsuccessfully in pilot projects against *Ae. aegypti, An. quadrimaculatus* and *C. p. fatigans*. In the case of *Ae. aegypti* more than four and a half million males were released, so that it will be appreciated that problems of logistics are formidable. It is generally felt that genetic methods should be employed only when reduction has been achieved, as far as possible, by other means. Chemosterilants present quite different problems since, in this case, the sterile males (and females) are derived from the existing population. Laboratory studies have been encouraging and a small pilot project, against *C. tarsalis* breeding in desert pools in California, met with partial success. However, toxicity to man and other mammals seems to pre-

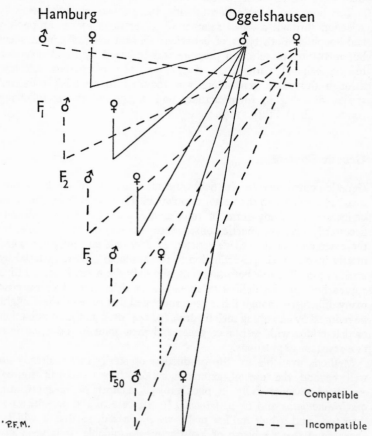

Fig. 39 Unidirectional compatibility between two west German strains of *Culex pipiens* var. *molestus*. The Hamburg mating type, derived from the original mother, is retained even after complete replacement of Hamburg by Ogglehausen chromosomes by breeding from Oggleshausen males through 50 generations. This suggests that mating type is determined by a cytoplasmic factor independent of nuclear control. The evidence for this, though considerable, is not conclusive. An alternative hypothesis postulates the existence of nuclear genes conditioning the cytoplasm coupled with meiotic drive leading to production of one type of male gamete only during spermatogenesis.

clude their distribution at all widely and it is generally felt that they may be most useful as substitutes for ionizing radiation in the mass production of sterile males.

A third potential source of sterile males is the F_1 male sterility which frequently results from crosses between members of sibling species complexes. Laboratory experiments with males of this type, produced by crossing members of the *An. gambiae* complex (p. 159), have shown them to exhibit enhanced longevity and mating competitiveness by contrast with normal males. Certain crosses have the advantage of producing 100 per cent males in the F_1. In view of these encouraging results a field experiment is planned, based on the seeding of natural breeding places with eggs from the appropriate cross. A computer analysis has revealed the the minimum required to secure clearance of breeding places would be daily introduction of one 'factory' egg per five natural eggs. It is estimated that, if a ratio of $1:1$ could be achieved, clearance would be possible in about nine weeks.

Up to the present the only fully successful pilot experiment has made use of a remarkable form of reproductive incompatibility found in various geographically representative populations of the *Culex pipiens* complex. Although certain alternatives, involving meiotic drive, have been suggested and cannot be entirely ruled out,[4] the simplest explanation of this type of incompatibility attributes it to a cytoplasmic factor independent of nuclear control (Fig. 39).

Whatever may be the nature of the factor concerned it appears to operate by preventing fusion of the sperm and egg nuclei. Parthenogenetic development frequently ensues but all but a very few embryos die before hatching. As Fig. 39 shows, the cytoplasm of one strain can be combined with the nuclear genom of another by repeated backcrossing to males of the latter. Males of a Paris-California hybrid strain, synthesized in this way and incompatible with Rangoon *C. p. fatigans,* were released in a village near Rangoon. After three months all egg rafts recovered were found to be sterile.[5] A comparable form of non-reciprocal fertility has been shown to occur in the *Aedes scutellaris* complex (p. 166) but this has been less fully investigated.

REFERENCES

1. KITZMILLER, J. B., 1953, 'Mosquito genetics and cytogenetics'. *Revta bras. Malar. Doenc. trop.,* **5**: 285-359.

2. DAVIDSON, G. & MASON, G. F., 1963, 'Genetics of mosquitoes'. *A. Rev. Ent.*, **8**: 177–196
3. KITZMILLER, J. B., 1963, 'Mosquito cytogenetics; a review of the literature'. *Bull. Wld Hlth Org.*, **29**: 345–355.
4. WRIGHT, J. W. & PAL, R. (Eds), 1967, *Genetics of Insect Vectors of Disease.* Amsterdam: Elsevier.
5. LAVEN, H., 1967, 'Eradication of *Culex pipiens fatigans* through cytoplasmic incompatibility'. *Nature, Lond.*, **216**: 383–384.

X

Species Complexes

The Anopheles maculipennis Complex

THIS is the classic mosquito species complex. It was the first to be recognized as such and is notable not only for the skill and perseverance directed to its elucidation but for the historic importance of these studies in revealing the potential importance for epidemiology of minutiae of vector biology.

The existence of biological heterogeneity in *'Anopheles maculipennis'* was recognized early in the present century but its practical implications began to be suspected only at the end of the First World War. The return of troops, at that time, from highly malarious regions was expected to result in widespread malaria. Instead, though outbreaks occurred, they remained remarkably localized. Many areas in which the supposed vector was abundant remained free from the disease, a situation known as 'Anophelism *sine* malaria' (Anophelism without malaria).

The detection of long-winged and short-winged forms of *'Anopheles maculipennis'* in Holland and their association with fresh and brackish breeding places respectively provided the first clue. Other studies, particularly in Italy, led to the discovery of other recognizable forms and the demonstration that these could be readily separated on the basis of their egg markings and float patterns. Ultimately detailed studies of behaviour, ecology and reproductive compatibility led to the following formal classification: *An. maculipennis* s.str., *An. labranchiae* and ssp. *atroparvus*, *An. messeae*, *An. melanoon* and var. *subalpinus*, *An. sacharovi* (= *An. elutus*). More recent studies, including detailed chromosome mapping, have served merely to confirm this classification.

An. maculipennis s.str. is widely distributed in Europe, extending east as far as western Siberia. It is a cold-resistant form, tending to predominate over the others in mountainous areas. *An. messeae* is even more widely distributed, extending into eastern USSR as far as the Zeya River. These two seem likely, on distributional grounds, to be the most closely related to the North American members of the complex. The only other form found in northern Europe, *An. labranchiae atroparvus*, is tolerant of brackish breeding places and predominates in coastal areas, while extending inland as far east as the Caspian Sea.

An. labranchiae s.str. resembles ssp. *atroparvus* biologically but has a more southerly distribution. The two are known to occur together only in a limited area in central Italy. Hybrid F_1 females are fertile, F_1 males usually sterile though sometimes, in part, fertile. *An. labranchiae* s.str. is essentially a western Mediterranean species, not known further east than Italy and Tunisia. *An. melanoon* and *subalpinus* are thought to be no more than varieties of the same species. Their joint range extends from southern Europe eastwards to the Caucasus and Iran. They are exclusively freshwater breeders, unlike *An. sacharovi* which favours brackish breeding places though also occurring in fresh waters from the eastern Mediterranean to as far east as Uzbekistan. This is the only member of the complex, in either hemisphere, still presenting problems as a malaria vector (in parts of Greece and Turkey).

New World members of the complex include three species, *An. aztecus, freeborni* and *occidentalis,* which are closely related to one another and to the Old World members. Other species having a more easterly distribution (Fig. 40) are also related, as shown by chromosome studies and crossing experiments, but less closely. These include *An. earlei, punctipennis* and *quadrimaculatus,* the last named being the most closely related to *An. freeborni* and its allies.

Certain other species occurring in the eastern United States have been included in the complex by some authors but their chromosomes have not yet been fully studied and their precise relationships must, for the moment, remain in doubt. Facts suggestive of a New World origin for the complex include the greater morphological divergences between New World members, the greater complexity of their chromosome banding, implying a large number of inversions, the virtual absence of synapsis in hybrid chromosome sets and the greater degree of chromosomal polymorphism, especially in *An. punctipennis*.

The fact that this species proves, on cytological evidence, to be quite closely related to the others is interesting. Unlike other species belonging, or closely related, to the complex it has brightly patterned wings recalling various species of *Anopheles* s.str. occurring in the New World tropics (Fig. 41). An origin of the dark-winged *Anopheles* s.str. of temperate latitudes from more brightly marked tropical ancestors accords well with current ideas regarding the evolution of *Anopheles* in general.

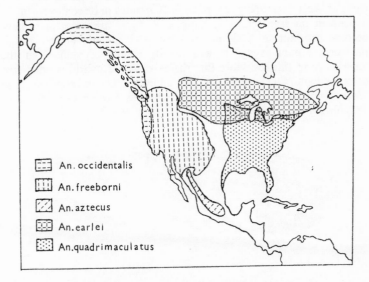

An. occidentalis
An. freeborni
An. aztecus
An. earlei
An. quadrimaculatus

Fig. 40 Distribution of the *Anopheles maculipennis* complex in the New World. (After Kitzmiller, Frizzi & Baker, ref. 4, p. 156.)

The Anopheles gambiae Complex

Two freshwater members of this complex occur together in many parts of Africa, including the type locality. It is not, at present, possible to say which is the type form since individuals can be identified with certainty only by the banding of the X-chromosomes in preparations from larval salivary glands (Fig. 42). It is therefore preferred to call them forms A and B. Crosses between them, in either direction, yield sterile F_1 males. The F_1 females, however, are fertile and back-crossing is possible to either parent form. The limited field evidence available suggests that hybridization resulting from back-crossing in nature is at most very rare and that the two forms might reasonably be regarded as distinct species.[1]

The only biological differences so far detected are related to climatic tolerances. *An. gambiae* B tends to predominate in drier parts of the range and is the only form so far found in Somalia and southwest Arabia. *An. gambiae* A generally predominates in more humid parts of the range and is the only freshwater form found in the wetter parts of West Africa (Fig. 43, p. 163). It appears to be somewhat more dependent on man than *An. gambiae* B. Both species seem to have become resistant to Dieldrin, in West Africa, more or less simultaneously around 1955. It was in the course of studies on the inheritance of this resistance that the existence of hybrid sterility first came to light. DDT resistance first appeared, in *An. gambiae* A, in West Africa at the end of 1967, apparently as a result of exposure to agricultural insecticide.

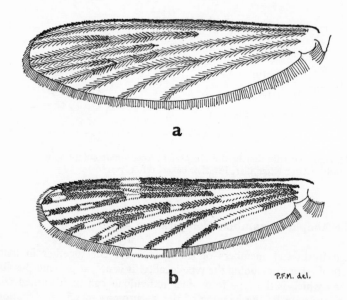

a

b   P.F.M. del.

Fig. 41 Wing patterns in related species of *Anopheles*. **a** *An. labranchiae atroparvus*. **b** *An. punctipennis*. Cytological and other evidence suggests that **b** is the more primitive.

A third freshwater member of the complex, *An. gambiae* C, was discovered in consequence of house-spraying with BHC in the Mazoe Valley in Rhodesia. Following the spraying *An. gambiae* almost

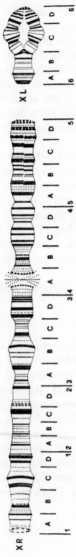

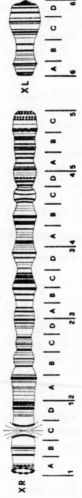

Fig. 42 Salivary gland X-chromosomes: *An. gambiae* A and *An. gambiae* B. The very conspicuous differences in banding offer much better diagnostic characters than any others at present available. The possibility of using these characters for identification in the field is currently being explored. (From Coluzzi, *Parassitologia*, 9: 73, 1967.)

entirely disappeared from houses although the outdoor population remained abundant. This gave rise to the suggestion that selection by the insecticide had led to the replacement of endophilic, anthropophilic *An. gambiae* A and B by exophilic, zoophilic forms of the same species. An alternative hypothesis was that the phenomenon was an ecological rather than a genetic one and that a third species possessing these characteristics was present and had previously been overlooked until the elimination of A and B by spraying drew attention to its presence. Crossing experiments showed that the latter explanation was the correct one. *An. gambiae* C has since been found in other parts of Rhodesia and in Swaziland and, recently, in Zanzibar and Pemba (Fig. 43).

The F_1 from crosses between males of *An. gambiae* A and B and females of *An. gambiae* C is characterized not only by male sterility but by gross distortion of the sex ratio resulting in the production of 80-90 per cent males. In crosses between males of A and B and females of the two brackish-water members of the complex, *An. melas* and *An. merus,* the effect is even more marked. The F_1 from these crosses comprises 98-100 per cent males. It is hoped to use F_1 eggs of this type in the exploratory experiments on genetic control previously mentioned (p. 155).

Other Anopheline Complexes

Combined taxonomic and ecological studies have revealed many other sibling species complexes in the genus *Anopheles*. Apart from some preliminary work on the *An. punctulatus* complex, which includes the major malaria vectors in the general area of Melanesia, none of these has been studied cytogenetically. Chromosomes of representative members of the two main series of *Nyssorhynchus*, the *An. albimanus* and *An. darlingi* series, have been examined and found, in some instances, to exhibit a high degree of chromosomal polymorphism. These should provide excellent cytogenetic material. At a more conventional taxonomic level several detailed microtaxonomic studies have been carried out, particularly in South-east Asia, which are models of their kind.[2, 3]

The Culex pipiens Complex[4]

Culex pipiens s.str. is a mosquito of temperate latitudes throughout the

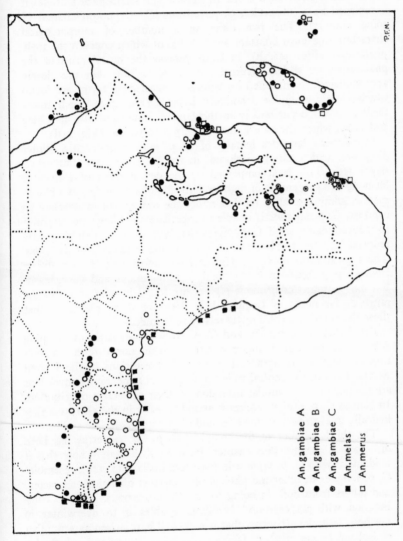

○ An.gambiae A
● An.gambiae B
◉ An.gambiae C
■ An.melas
□ An.merus

P.F.M.

Fig. 43 Distribution of the *Anopheles gambiae* complex. At the time of writing some 1,850 identifications have been made from 36 different countries, nearly 1,150 of them by crossing experiments.

holarctic and of high altitudes in East and West Africa and lower altitudes in South Africa. It is also said to occur in Argentina although it has been little studied there. In tropical and subtropical latitudes it is replaced by a subspecies, *C. p. fatigans* (*C. p. quinquefasciatus* of some authors). The two differ in a number of morphological characters, the most constant and reliable of which concern the male phallosome (Fig. 44a, b). In *C. p. pipiens* the dorsal arms of the phallosome are widely divergent. In *C. p. fatigans* they are closely approximated. In intermediate latitudes intermediate forms are found which closely resemble laboratory hybrids (Fig. 44c). Such intermediate forms occur widely in the United States and also in China and Japan where they are known as *C. p. var. pallens* (Fig. 44d).

In northern latitudes females of *C. p. pipiens* undergo a winter disapause, which can be induced, in the laboratory, by diminished day length. This is accompanied by the development of a massive fat-body and suspension of flight activity and blood-feeding. If a blood-meal is administered in the laboratory the ovaries fail to develop. In contrast, *C. p. fatigans* is unable to hibernate and shows no response to reduced photoperiod. *C. p. pipiens* has been shown to exhibit greatly reduced response to photoperiod in more southerly parts of its range. The typical form of *C. p. pipiens* from north-west Europe differs from *C. p. fatigans* in being highly ornithophilous and eurygamous but man-biting, stenogamous *pipiens* are found in other parts of the range as far north as Leningrad. It does not seem, therefore, that these characteristics are directly related to latitude.

Belief that *C. p. pipiens* and *C. p. fatigans* are partly overlapping subspecies, distributed chiefly in relation to the north-south temperature gradient, is strengthened by several observations in the United States. Thus in the central valley of California temperature inversions are accompanied by similar inversions in their respective distribution. In Kansas *C. p. pipiens* are most abundant early in the year, morphologically intermediate forms later and *C. p. fatigans* in late summer.

The third member of the complex, *C. p. var. molestus* has been discussed in the previous chapter. Here we shall merely note that it is identical with *C. p. pipiens* in male terminalia (Fig. 37e), resembles *C. p. fatigans* in other morphological, and most biological, characters and differs from both in being frequently autogenous. This, in combination with underground breeding, enables it to overwinter in northern latitudes. It seems that it may well have arisen as a number of isolated relicts of *C. p. fatigans*, the latter having formerly had a more northerly distribution extending into southern Europe.

The situation in Australia is complicated and not yet fully under-

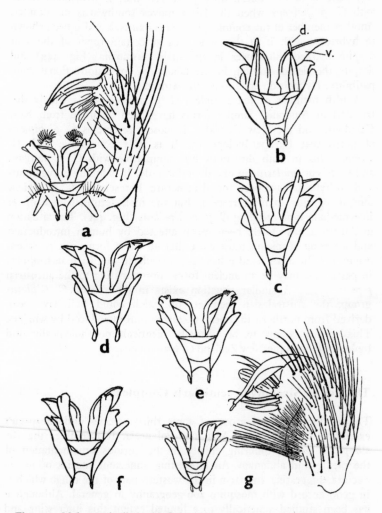

Fig. 44 Male terminalia in the *Culex pipiens* complex. **a** *C. pipiens pipiens.*
b *C. p. fatigans.* **c** *C. p. pipiens* × *C. p. fatigans* F. hybrid. **d** *C. p. var.
pallens.* **e** *C. p. var. molestus.* **f** *C. p. australicus.* **g** *C. globocoxitus.*

stood. *C. p. var. molestus* is common in the Melbourne area, where it may have been introduced during the last war. It hybridizes freely with *C. p. fatigans* when the latter moves southwards in summer. Another member of the complex, *C. globocoxitus*, has also been shown to hybridize with it in the same area at certain times of the year despite marked differences in the male terminalia (Fig. 44g) and despite the demonstration, in the laboratory, of unidirectional compatibility. Hybrids do not survive the winter.

A fifth member of the complex, *C. p. australicus*, is widely distributed in Australia. Similar forms have been recorded from New Caledonia and the New Hebrides. It closely resembles *C. p. pipiens* of north-west Europe biologically. It is fully compatible with *C. globocoxitus* in both directions but compatible with *C. p. fatigans* and *C. p. var. molestus* in one direction only. It is highly eurygamous and no hybrids have been found in nature. It resembles *C. p. pipiens* morphologically in most respects but the male terminalia are of an intermediate type recalling *C. p. var. pallens* (Fig. 44f). The situation in Australia has clearly been much affected by human introduction and a strong suspicion must exist that all these forms are of recent origin. On the other hand it has been speculated that *C. p. australicus*, in particular, may be an ancient form approximating to the ancestrial *pipiens* stock. A similar situation exists in the related *C. trifilatus* group, the Australasian members of which could well have been derived from northern European *C. torrentium* introduced by whalers. This species seems to be virtually identical morphologically and biologically with the New Zealand *C. pervigilans*.

The Aedes (Stegomyia) scutellaris Complex[5]

This a closely related group of some thirty species and subspecies extending from southern Asia into Polynesia. It resembles the *Ae. albopictus* group, differing chiefly in the curious ornamentation of the pleura and abdomen. An interesting annectent species occurs in Socotra, suggesting an origin in the western part of the range which is in good accord with mosquito zoo-geography in general. Although it has been studied genetically to a limited extent this interesting and important group needs more attention. One subspecies, *Ae. pseudoscutellaris*, is restricted, so far as is known, to Fiji, where it occurs in both coastal and inland areas. It is represented elsewhere in the Pacific by a widely distributed subspecies, *Ae. ps. polynesiensis*, which has clearly been disseminated by man and is, as we already noted (pp. 47,

48), the principal vector of the subperiodic form of wuchererian filariasis. It has apparently been reintroduced into Fiji where it is found only in coastal areas. Although it has diverged morphologically to a limited extent it remains reproductively compatible in both directions with the type form (with somewhat reduced hatching of F_1 eggs). Males of both forms also show a partial preference for females of their own kind. The extent to which this limits hybridization in Fiji has not been investigaged. F_2 and F_3 hybrids are fully vigorous and fertile.

Ae. scutellaris is considered, subject to future genetic study, to extend from the extreme western part of the range eastwards to Melanesia. As was noted previously (p. 155) an interesting undirectional compatibility exists between this and *Ae. scutellaris katherinensis*, a subspecies found in the Cape York peninsula. The so-called *Ae. hebrideus*, from the New Hebrides, resembles *Ae. scutellaris* so closely that it may well be an introduced form of the latter. No crosses have been made though *Ae. hebrideus* has been crossed on a small scale with the sympatric *Ae. pernotatus*. This cross revealed a limited compatibility in one direction only. The F_1 were all female and resembled the mother (*hebrideus*) morphologically. The back-cross to male *pernotatus* produced a small number of viable males resembling the father in their terminalia and intermediate in other morphological characters. Crosses between *Ae. scutellaris*, and ssp. *katherinensis*, and *Ae. ps. polynesiensis* are sterile in both directions. We thus seem to glimpse the existence of two species complexes, one in Melanesia, the other in Polynesia. Beyond this, in the absence of further genetic studies, we cannot go.

Other medically important species complexes are *Ae. albopictus* and its allies and *Ae. africanus* and *Haemagogus spegazzinii* and theirs. None of these have been studied genetically. Some preliminary work has been done on the very important *C. vishnui* complex, including *C. tritaeniorhynchus* (p. 65) but no results are yet available. Very little has been done with *Mansonia* but, interestingly, it has been shown that *M. uniformis* from Africa and from Malaya remain fully compatible.

REFERENCES

1. MATTINGLY, P. F., DAVIDSON, G., MASON, G. F., PATERSON, H. F., COLUZZI, M., COZ, J., HAMON, J. & GIGLIOLI, M. E. C., 1964, 'The *Anopheles gambiae* complex'. *Riv. Malar.*, **43**: 165–275.

2. COLLESS, D. H., 1956, 'The *Anopheles leucosphyrus* group'. *Trans. R. ent. Soc. Lond.*, **108**: 37–116.
3. REID, J. A., 1962, 'The *Anopheles barbirostris* group (Diptera, Culicidae)'. *Bull. ent. Res.*, **53**: 1–57.
4. MATTINGLY, P. F., ROZENBOOM, L. E., KNIGHT, K. L., LAVEN, H., DRUMMOND, F. H., CHRISTOPHERS, S. R. & SHUTE, P. G., 1951, 'The *Culex pipiens* complex'. *Trans. R. ent. Soc. Lond.*, **102**: 331–382.
5. MARKS, E. N., 1954, 'A review of the *Aedes scutellaris* subgroup with a study of variation in *Aedes pseudoscutellaris* (Theobald) (Diptera: Culicidae)'. *Bull. Br. Mus. nat. Hist. Ent.*, **3**: 349–414.

a

PLATE IX   *b*

Daytime resting places. Some kinds of mosquitoes prefer these to be dark and humid, but not all.

a.   A favoured resting site of *Anopheles maculatus* in Malaya. Damper and denser vegetation along stream banks was much less productive (from Wharton, *Med. J. Malaya.*, **4**: 263, 1950).

b.   Open grass savanna in South America may harbour mosquitoes in densities of the order 3 million per sq. km. The sweep-nets shown were used for collecting mosquitoes flying above the grass after dark (from Zulueta, *Am. J. trop. Med.*, **30**: 334, 1950).

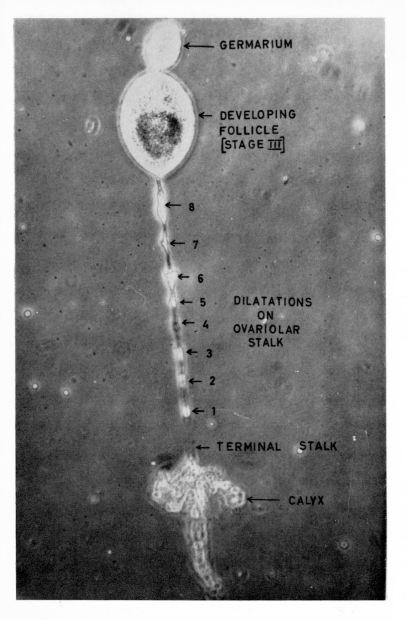

GERMARIUM

DEVELOPING
FOLLICLE
[STAGE III]

← 8
← 7
← 6
← 5
← 4
← 3
← 2
← 1

DILATATIONS
ON
OVARIOLAR
STALK

TERMINAL STALK

CALYX

PLATE X

Isolated ovariole from an *Anopheles gambiae* which has passed through at least eight gonotropic cycles. The minimum age of such an individual can be calculated, granted a knowledge of the duration of each cycle under the conditions prevailing. From the distribution of the different age groups in the population a life-expectancy curve for the population can be constructed (from Gillies and Wilkes, *Bull. ent. Res.*, **56**: 262, 1965).

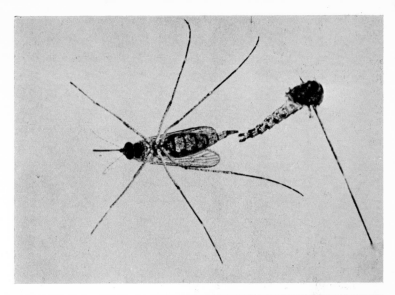

a

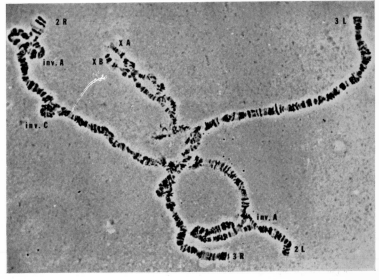

b

PLATE XI

a. Artificial mating of *Aedes mariae*. The female is anaesthetized and laid on her back. The male is decapitated and has his wings and legs removed. He can be either impaled on a needle, as shown, gummed to a paper point or held by suction to the end of a narrow-bore tube.

(*Photo: Mario Coluzzi*).

b. Salivary gland chromosomes of an *Anopheles gambiae* A × *An. gambiae* B female hybrid. Note in particular the extensive asynaptic regions in the X-chromosomes and the extensive inversions in both arms of chromosome 2 (from G. Davidson, H. E. Paterson, M. Coluzzi, G. F. Mason and D. W. Micks, 'The *Anopheles gambiae* complex', in J. W. Wright and R. Pal (Eds), *Genetics of Insect Vectors of Disease*, pp. 211-249, fig. 12, Elsevier, Amsterdam, 1967).

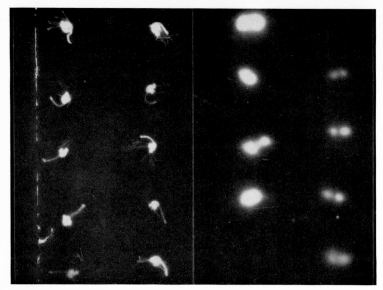

a

b

PLATE XII

a. Detection of marked mosquitoes by autoradiography. Marking is by means of radio-isotopes fed to the larvae. When applied to strips of X-ray film, mosquitoes labelled with a hard isotope, in this case P^{32}, give a blurred image. Those marked with a soft isotope (S^{35}) give a sharp image. It is thus possible to identify, in simultaneous recaptures, mosquitoes from two different releases (from X-ray film, courtesy M. T. Gillies).

b. An experimental hut. Each wall has an identical window, which can be fitted with an entry or exit trap. In the latter case entry is permitted by raising the bottom of the blind covering the door a short distance above the ground. The walls have detachable linings, which can be treated with insecticide if desired. Alternatively, knockdown catches can be made with pyrethrum. The whole is surrounded by a concrete ant ditch.

(Photo: Author).

XI

Retrospect and Prospect

THE failure of Manson's discovery (p. 48) to bear more immediate fruit seems to have arisen chiefly from deficiencies in the notions then prevailing concerning mosquito biology. Neither Manson nor his entomological contemporaries could bring themselves to regard mosquitoes as sufficiently long-lived to serve as other than temporary, passive nurseries for the parasite.[1] The next essential step, realization of the role of the mosquito as an active transmitter *by bite,* had to await Ross's discoveries twenty years later. During those twenty years Manson continued to believe that infection of the human host by *Wuchereria* came from the corpses of mosquitoes drowned in domestic water. Primed by Manson, Ross began his researches, in 1894, under the firm impression that the same course of events was involved in the transmission of malaria. His task thus seemed the simple one of identifying the resting stages of the parasite in the mosquito, observing any changes in its appearance after liberation into the water and so learning to identify potentially infective bodies of water.[2]

None of this need greatly have mattered had Ross been aware of two other aspects of mosquito biology—vector specificity and the comparative exophily of anopheline malaria vectors in contrast to the common domestic culicines. As it was there followed two laborious, and fruitless, years of feeding domestic mosquitoes (*Ae. aegypti, C. p. fatigans*) on infected patients varied by dosing others, uninfected, with infusions of drowned mosquitoes. Finally, as doubts began to grow, came a visit, on leave, to the Nilgiri Hills and the discovery of an intensely malarious valley, running down from Ootacamund, where there was no storage of domestic water, all being obtained fresh from springs and hill streams. Here Ross noticed, for the first time, an anopheline mosquito, a single individual during the whole of his stay, and began to realize for the first time the possibility of a surreptitious,

M

exophilic vector and one which, moreover, bred not in stored water but in some hitherto-undetected natural breeding place.

Back to Secunderabad Ross turned his attention to 'dappled-winged' mosquitoes. The species most abundant in and around houses (*An. vagus*) proved reluctant to feed but an assistant, dispatched to hunt for breeding places, brought pupae of another species, no longer identifiable. Within a few days the search was over. Adults duly emerged and in two of these, some days after feeding, oocysts were at last observed. Transferred to Calcutta, Ross was unable to obtain human volunteers for further experiments. Accordingly he turned his attention to avian malaria and within a year had demonstrated sporozoites in the salivary glands. Even then he himself continued to believe that dissemination by spores was the primary mode of transmission, with transmission by bite playing only a secondary role. A visit to Sierra Leone years later, and a confrontation with *An. gambiae*, was required to convince him of the true potentialities of the vector.

Others, however, had already seen the writing on the wall. Formation of the Royal Society malaria committee in 1899, and the dispatch of Christophers and Stephens to India[3] led in less than three years to the laying down of the main outlines of the malaria picture as it appears to us today. Ross's unhappy experiences had at least the merit of emphasizing the importance of vector specificity and already in 1899 the materials for Theobald's great monograph of the Culicidae were being assembled under the auspices of the Colonial Office (Fig. 45).

Yellow Fever and the Idea of Zoonosis

Neither Manson's nor Ross's discoveries could have been made without prior identification of the blood stages of the parasite (by Lewis, in 1872, in the case of *W. bancrofti* and by Laveran, in 1880, in the case of *P. vivax*). With yellow fever the situation was quite otherwise. The involvement of *Ae. aegypti* as vector was correctly deduced, on epidemiological grounds, by Carlos Finlay in 1881 and partly confirmed by him by artificial transmission. It was, however, only with the advent of Ross's discoveries that his suggestions began to be taken seriously. They were finally confirmed experimentally, by transmission to volunteers, by Walter Reed in 1901. Even then the authorities remained unconvinced that mosquitoes could provide more than a secondary mode of transmission until a successful anti-mosquito campaign in Havana in the same year brought conviction.

Downing Street,

6th December, 1898.

Sir,

In my Circular of the 19th of August, last, I referred to an intended investigation of Malaria.

A Commission has now been appointed for the purpose and is about to procede to Africa.

The Commissioners will report, from time to time, to a Committee appointed jointly by the Royal Society and myself, who will exercise a general supervision over the enquiry.

It has been suggested by this Committee, that, in view of the possible connection of Malaria with mosquitoes, it is desirable to obtain exact knowledge of the different species of mosquitoes and allied insects in the various tropical Colonies. I will therefore ask you, if there are facilities for the purpose, to be good enough to take the necessary steps at your convenience to have collections made of the winged insects in the Colony which bite men or animals.

I enclose a printed copy of directions which have been drawn up by the British Museum for the guidance of those who may be employed on the work, and would add that several specimens of each kind of insect should be obtained and that they should be sent direct to the British Museum (Natural History), Cromwell Road, London, S.W., to be examined and classified. A first series of the specimens will be retained by the Museum, whilst the duplicates will be available for distribution as may be desired.

As the question of the scientific investigation of Malaria is one to which I attach great importance, I trust that every effort will be made to carry out as speedily and as thoroughly as possible the directions contained in this despatch.

I have the honour to be,
Sir,
Your most obedient, humble Servant,

The Officer Administrating
the Government of

J. CHAMBERLAIN,

Fig. 45 Circular letter from the Secretary of State for the Colonies, Mr Joseph Chamberlain, to persons administering Britain's overseas territories. Manson's epochal discovery was followed by twenty years of silence. Not so Ross's which was made in the same year that this circular was printed.

Other successful campaigns followed in Panama, New Orleans and elsewhere in the New World, so that before long the idea was firmly established that maintenance of the causative agent (still unidentified) was dependent exclusively on the presence of sufficient numbers of human non-immunes and a sufficient density of *Ae. aegypti* to maintain transmission. As against this, experimental evidence of transmission to a chimpanzee was already available in 1909 and Manson, among others, warned of the possibility of a non-human primate reservoir. Successes, however, continued to accumulate and in 1915 the Rockefeller Foundation became committed to a scheme for the eradication of the disease from both hemispheres by reduction of the urban vector.

All then went well until, in 1926, the introduction of non-immune troops into north-eastern Brazil was followed by an extensive rural outbreak of *aegypti*-borne yellow fever. Worse was to follow when, in 1928, an outbreak occurred in Rio de Janeiro, the first for twenty years, and subsequent investigations revealed the presence of rural non-*aegypti*-borne yellow fever and, later, of jungle yellow fever in forest primates. During the early '30s development of the viscerotome, permitting the taking of post mortem liver samples by non-medical personnel, and of the white mouse as laboratory host, permitted the widespread surveys and laboratory transmission experiments on which our present, still imperfect, knowledge depends.

Final isolation and identification of the causative organism of yellow fever took place in the laboratories of the Rockefeller West Africa Yellow Fever Commission in 1928. A key factor was the importation of rhesus monkeys, which provided the first susceptible laboratory host. Realization of the great variety of other arboviruses came much later and only after initial prejudices had been overcome. Outstanding in the history of these discoveries was the recognition, by Lumsden, of the involvement of mosquitoes in the classic outbreak of St Louis encephalitis in the city of that name in 1933, the vigorous opposition to his arguments by officialdom, and the honour finally paid to his memory by the posthumous republication of his paper a quarter of a century later.

The Dawning of the Idea of Eradication

The battle of man with mosquitoes goes back far beyond the discovery of their involvement with disease. Mosquito nets were known to the Romans (who thought them rather effeminate) and personal protection by fire smoke was and is practised by primitive peoples. No great leap was involved in the transition to adulticides. These were already employed in the classic yellow fever campaign in Havana at the beginning of the century (p. 170), among them tobacco smoke used to avoid contamination in the cigar warehouses. Bonification involving large-scale drainage and land-reclamation derived partial economic justification from the resultant decrease in malaria long before the causes of the latter were known.

Limited campaigns directed specifically to malaria reduction called for more sophisticated techniques. Malcolm Watson achieved an outstanding success against *An. sundaicus* at Port Swettenham in 1901, though he cannot even have known with which vector he was dealing. Other successes followed, in the coastal lowlands, by virtue of forest-clearing, but in the highlands the same technique merely made matters worse by encouraging the proliferation of *An. maculatus*. Control was finally achieved by subsoil drainage but not until a valuable lesson had been learnt regarding the multiformity of vector behaviour. Even then many years were to pass before the claims of the entomologist to equal partnership in control campaigns began to be accepted. With certain notable exceptions (ref. 4, p. 101) malaria control on any scale remained essentially an affair of drains, augmented by larviciding with oil or paris green and, from the middle '30s on, some space-spraying with pyrethrum, until the coming of residual insecticides (Fig. 46).

The first attempt at all-out vector eradication seems to have been an onslaught on *Ae. aegypti* in north-eastern Brazil, in 1927-29, following on the yellow fever epidemic in that area noted above. It failed as did other attempts in Brazilian cities, giving rise to the theory of an irreducible minimum of vector population which would render total eradication impossible. Yet it was in that same country, a few years later, that the first, and very nearly the only, total eradication of a mosquito species was achieved.

Anopheles gambiae was introduced into Brazil, probably by fast mail-carrying destroyers from Dakar, early in 1930.[4] Devastating epidemics followed in Natal and although these were suppressed by the use of paris green as a larvicide the vector gained a foothold and began a sureptitious spread northwards along the coast. In 1938 came an irruption into previously malaria-free inland valleys and a mortality as heavy as any ever recorded. At its greatest the area involved was some 12,000 square miles. By the combined efforts of the Rockefeller Foundation and the Brazilian government this area was totally cleared in a little under two years, using paris green in combination with pyrethrum for house-spraying, at a cost of some two million dollars.

Fig. 46 The Spirit of Belmont Road. The malariologist J. W. S. Macfie as seen by his friend at the Liverpool School of Tropical Medicine, Sir Clive Foster Cooper. Early successes in the control of malaria by large-scale drainage led to some confusion (not always entirely genuine) between malariology and sanitary engineering. Manson's contemporaries called him 'Mosquito Manson' and tapped their foreheads. Ross's contemporaries held their noses. (From a water-colour in the British Museum (Natural History).)

Nothing can have done more than this campaign, and another like it, against *An. gambiae* in Egypt in 1944, to generate the wave of euphoria which accompanied the introduction of DDT but, once again, a discarding of old ideas and a new level of sophistication were required before the new weapon could be exploited to real advantage. Even the elementary theory of eradication had to be learnt. The idea of a once and for all interruption of transmission came slowly and the first report of the WHO Expert Committee on Malaria contains the words 'DDT probably will have to be used as a recurring measure, similar to the use of chlorine in water supplies.'[5] (It is, after all, a chlorinated hydrocarbon!). Echoes of the Rio de Janeiro yellow fever epidemic (p. 172) may have helped to inspire the spectacular campaign for the eradication (as opposed to the simple reduction) of *An. labranchiae* in Sardinia[6] but this campaign, though failing in its primary objective, sufficed to show once and for all that total vector eradication is not required to secure the interruption of transmission and is, in any case, seldom likely to be feasible except in the case of highly domesticated culicines.

By the time of the launching of the world-wide malaria eradication campaign, at the eighth World Health Assembly in Mexico in 1955, yet another level of sophistication had been attained, though it may be doubted that this was altogether realized by those by whom the programme was framed. Residual insecticides, on the scale on which it was planned to use them, are selective agents of enormous potency. By reason of the physiological and behavioural plasticity of vector populations it had ceased to be sufficient to think like a mosquito and had become necessary to think like a population of mosquitoes. The first case of insecticide resistance in *Anopheles* had been reported in 1951, and exophily, leading to insecticide avoidance, had already been demonstrated on a number of occasions. An example of their devastating impact was the virtual abandonment of attempts at eradication in tropical Africa less than ten years after the global campaign was launched.

Yet these do not, in themselves, preclude the interruption of transmission. They merely restrict the ways in which it may be brought about. We have a whole armoury of weapons at our disposal. What are lacking are the skills, motivations and administrative structures needed for their effective employment. And so we are brought to a yet higher level of sophistication at which man himself is included in the biological context (from which the biologist himself is not wholly guiltless of trying to exclude him). If we are nearer to the realization of the hopes held at the launching of the world-wide malaria campaign nearly fifteen years ago it is not because of any technical advances, though these have certainly occurred, but because we have learned by experience the nature of the problems involved. Success when it comes, in the century ahead, will depend on convincing the biologist that, to paraphrase a little, 'a proper study of mankind is man' and the administrator that his problems are problems of human ecology not to be solved merely by the contemplation of his own image.[7]

Present and Future Prospect

The future of mosquito-borne disease is in the hands of man. We shall not try to predict it. All that will be attempted is a sketch of the present prospect and some general suggestions as to how future prospects might be brightened.

The earliest counter to mosquito-borne disease must have been simple avoidance – running away. The word 'malaria' carries echoes from the time when this was man's only weapon. It is a good one, though seldom now available. As human populations pullulate it will become less so. Far from avoiding mosquito-borne disease man is likely increasingly to invite it by encroachment into environments previously unexploited. Even so, one form of avoidance will still be available—the avoidance of man-made disease. Penetration of the white man into the tropics and the road-building and railway-building which this involved have contributed enormously, by disturbance of natural drainage, to the burden of mosquito-borne disease. Intensive cultivation has taken added toll. This is now realized and to an increasing extent the planning of such projects takes note of hazards to health. The process will no doubt continue and, granted adequate research, there is no reason why such projects should not contribute positively to the improvement of human health rather than, as formerly, the reverse.

The same argument applies to the ravages wrought by uncontrolled urbanization and industrialization, but here the prospects for avoidance seem bleak. Attention is being, and must be, concentrated on vector reduction, either by simple sanitation (often abandoned with the advent of DDT) or by the use of larvicides. Some of these (Abate, Fenthion) have achieved dramatic success. Others are in the pipeline for use should resistance develop. Many believe this to be inevitable, the speed of its coming being in direct proportion to reduction of vector population. Even so it seems a wise precaution, which should have been observed from the first, to use such weapons only to the point at which resistance is not provoked and to supplement them to the greatest possible extent by alternative measures.

Among such measures the various forms of biological control have already been discussed. But these, for all their promise, also have their limitations, especially where, as is often the case, they are density-dependent. It is logical, therefore, while employing both types of vector control, to supplement them with a third category of weapons sufficiently distinct to avoid their disadvantages even though possessing others of their own. Such weapons are available in the form of vaccines and drugs depending not on any effect which they may have on the vector but on a direct attack on the parasite.

Lack of space has so far forbidden any discussion of drugs. Yet the subject is full of biological interest and this book would be sadly incomplete were it altogether ignored. The acquaintance of the Peruvians with cinchona bark, prior to the Spanish conquest, is disputed. It is a subject with an obvious bearing on the question of pre-Columbian malaria (p. 58). The action of the purified extract (quinine) on a variety of Protozoa led to the suspicion that malaria was a protozoal disease well before the discovery of the parasite. The complete synthesis of quinine was not achieved until 1944 and has never been commercially feasible. The essential feature of its structure (presence of the quinoline nucleus) was already known before 1850, but the first acceptable substitutes were not developed for some eighty years. Loss of the sources of quinine in Indonesia, during the Second World War, led to its replacement by the synthetic substitute mepacrine (atebrin) but this, like its modern, improved, counterpart, chloroquine, shares the principle defects of quinine, namely absence of destructive effect on gametocytes, rendering it ineffective for the interruption of transmission, and failure to affect tissue stages and so to prevent relapses in *vivax* or quartan infections. Resistance of *P. falciparum* to chloroquine in parts of South America and South-east Asia has created an urgent need for structurally unrelated drugs which are not subject to cross-resistance.

Chloroquine is a four-aminoquinoline. In a different class are the eight-aminoquinolines, notably primaquine, which are active against both tissue stages and gametocytes. These are used in the radical cure of relapsing infections and have a potential utility in the interruption of transmission by destruction of gametocytes. A third group, also active against tissue stages and gametocytes, includes pyrimethamine, the action of which is strongly reinforced by sulphonamides. It might thus seem that we already possess an armoury of drugs adequate for all purposes (setting aside the question of resistance which is still, in general, incomplete and of restricted occurrence). This, however, would be to ignore the human element and the very difficult problems of logistics raised by the mass distribution of drugs requiring constant, repetitive administration. Two comparatively new approaches may be of help in this connection. One is the large-scale distribution of chloroquine in the form of medicated cooking salt, already used with some success but presenting the problem of persuading people to use it, especially when the immediate threat of disease appears to recede. The other is the use of repository drugs which can be implanted under the skin and will continue to exert their effects for periods measurable in months. Such drugs, however, still require extensive testing before the risks of side-effects and of the development of resistance can be adequately assessed.

In the case of filariasis, experience has shown that the most effective method of control is the mass administration of drugs coupled with as extensive a reduction of the vector as possible. A control campaign on these lines, in Tahiti, employing the microfilaricide diethylcarba-mazine (Hetrazan, Banocide), has met with a large degree of success, though falling short of final eradication. However, problems of logistics and of public relations, arising from the necessity for repeated dosage over a long period and the occurrence, in a proportion of cases, of febrile side-reactions, are even more formidable than those associated with the control of malaria. The need in this case is for a drug which is easier to administer and which destroys adults as well as microfilariae. Diethylcarbamazine has recently been administered on a small scale, with some success, in the form of medicated salt.

So far as the arboviruses are concerned, chemotherapy is in its infancy. Live vaccines, conferring relatively rapid and long-lasting immunity, are available only for yellow fever. Besides the cost and research effort involved their production, testing is accompanied by considerable risks. It is even stated, on good authority, that had we known as much as we do now about these risks, the yellow fever vaccines might never have been produced, despite their proven safety and immense life-saving potential. A number of inactivated vaccines are available for use in special circumstances, but their effect is relatively short-lived and the lengthy period elapsing before they confer protection restricts their usefulness in epidemics. Vector reduction has had its successes in economically favourable circumstances, as against *Culex tarsalis* in the central valley of California, and where the vector is closely dependent on man, as with *Aedes aegypti* in the Americas. There can surely be little excuse for failure to control this species, at least under urban conditions, in Africa and Asia. In general, however, the path to the control of these diseases seems inevitably to be a long one, with no simple solution in view.

Present knowledge and experience do not encourage much faith in ultimate weapons. Success is more likely to come from integrated approaches making the best use of weapons of every kind. Computers can assist in the framing of such programmes and have already, to some extent, done so. But this alone is not enough. Behind the computers must be minds attuned to the biological realities and the diversity of elements in even the simplest ecological system. Mosquitoes are unlikely to surrender to elephants unless these have a Hannibal to lead them.

REFERENCES

1. MANSON, P., 1878, 'On the development of *Filaria sanguinis hominis*, and on the mosquito considered as a nurse'. *J. Linn. Soc. (Zool)*, **14**: 304–311.
2. ROSS, R., 1904, 'Researches on malaria'. *Les Prix Nobel*, 1902. Stockholm.
3. DANIELS, C. W., STEPHENS, J. W. W., CHRISTOPHERS, S. R., THEOBALD, F. V. LANKESTER, E. R. & JAMES, S. P., 1900-1903, *Reports to the Royal Society Malaria Committee*. London: Harrison & Sons.
4. SOPER, F. L. & WILSON, D. B., 1943, *Anopheles gambiae in Brazil*. New York: Rockefeller Foundation.
5. PAMPANA, E., 1963, *A Textbook of Malaria Eradication*. Oxford University Press.
6. LOGAN, J. A., 1933, *The Sardinian Project*. Baltimore: Johns Hopkins Press.
7. MANSELL PROTHERO, R., 1965, *Migrants and Malaria*. London: Longmans, Green & Co.

Appendix

NOTES ON THE LITERATURE

More than a thousand papers relating to mosquitoes and mosquito-borne disease are published every year, to say nothing of the many cyclostyled working documents circulated in conditions falling short of actual publication. The literature is thus very extensive indeed. Fortunately there is no shortage of books and review articles, with the aid of which it is possible to keep reasonably up to date. For very recent papers recourse must be had to monthly bibliographies, the most useful of which are the *Bulletin Signaletique d'Entomologie Médicale et Véterinaire*, published by the Office de la Recherche Scientifique et Technique Outre-mer in Paris and the Monthly bibliography of the US Department of Agriculture. Abstracting journals include, among others, the *Review of Applied Entomology*, Series B, and the *Tropical Diseases Bulletin*.

In the short-list of references at the end of each chapter of this book we have confined ourselves mainly to books and review articles. These will provide an adequate source of references for many purposes. However there is so much active research on mosquito biology, in particular, that any review article is liable to be seriously out of date. The following papers relate to subjects of topical interest mentioned in Chapter VII.

Circadian larval respiration rhythm in *C. pipiens:* Buffington, *Mosquito News*, **28**: 95, 1968

Pupation rhythm in *Ae. taeniorhynchus:* Nayar, *Ann. ent. Soc. Am.*, **60**: 946, 1967.

Seasonal migrations in *An. freeborni:* Baily & Baerg, *Proc. Pap. Calif. Mosq. Contr. Ass.*, **35**: 55, 1967.

General aspects of cyclical behaviour': Corbet, *Roy. ent. Soc. Lond. Symposia*, **3**: 13, 1966.

Flight activity in relation to biting activity: Corbet, *Trans. R. ent. Soc. Lond.*, **113**: 301, 1961 and Knight & Henderson, *J. Ga. ent. Soc.*, **2**: 63, 1967.

Swarming in *An. stephensi:*' Quraishi, *J. econ. Ent.*, **58**: 821, 1965.

Trap based on visual response of swarming males: Fay, *Mosquito News*, **28**: 1, 1968.

Mating barriers in the *C. pipiens* complex: Spielman, *Am. J. Hyg.*, **80**: 175, 1964.

Laboratory mating in *Ae. triseriatus:* Wright et al., *Ann. ent. Soc. Am.*, **59**: 1110, 1966.

Mating in *Opifex* and Deinocerites: Provost & Haeger, *Ann. ent. Soc. Am.*, **60**: 565, 1967.

Mating in *Deinocerites pseudes:* Galindo, *Mosquito News*, **37**: 187, 1967.

Male and female pheromones: Kliewer et al., *Ann. ent. Soc. Am.*, **59**: 530, 1966 and Gjullin et al., *Mosquito News*, **27**: 382, 1967.

Resistance of immature females to insemination: Lea, *J. Insect Physoil.*, **14**: 305, 1968.

Automatic recording of activity rhythms: Jones et al., *J. exp. Biol.*, **47**: 503, 1967 and Chiba, *Sci. Rep. Tohôku Univ.* Ser. 4, **32**: 97, 105 and 197, 1966.

Flower-feeding: Abdel-Malek, *Bull. Wld Hlth Org.*, **30**: 137, 1964 and see *A. Rep. E. Afr. Virus Res. Inst.*, in press.

Effects of temperature and photoperiod on autogeny in *C. tarsalis*: Logen & Harwood, *Mosquito News*, **25**: 462, 1965.

Reactions of ovipositing females to bacteria: Hazard et al., *Mosquito News*, **27**: 133, 1967 and Scherck & James, *Mosquito News*, **28**: 33, 1968.

Reactions of these to inorganic salts: Petersen & Rees, *Ibid*, p. 136.

Oviposition cycle of *C. p. pallens*: Oda, *Trop. Med. (Nagasaki)*, **9**: 39, 1967.

Behaviour changes in *An. pseudopunctipennis*: Palacios & Zulueta, *Nature, Lond.*, **203**: 940, 1964.

House entry in *An. balabacensis*: Scanlon & Sandinhand, *J. med. Ent.*, **2**: 61, 1965.

Daytime resting: Gjullin et al., *Mosquito News*, **23**: 203, 1963.

Effect of temperature and photoperiod on winter diapause: Kappus & Venard, *J. Insect Physiol.*, **13**: 1007, 1967.

Behavioural and genetical aspects of insecticide avoidance: Gerold & Laarman, *Nature, Lond.*, **215**: 518, 1967.

Nectar feeding: McCrae et al., *Ann. Rep. E. Afr. Virus Res. Inst.*, **17**: 64, 1968.

General problems of sampling: Muirhead-Thomson, *Ecology of Insect Vector Populations*. Academic Press, 1968.

Index